MW00613134

Janice N. Tobias
224 Ball Creek Rd.
Talking Rock, GA 30175

A COLLECTOR'S GUIDE TO

BLACK GLASS 2

BY MARLENA TOOHEY

Credits

Photography on pages 18, 20–21, 26–28, 31–33, 37–39, 42, 57–62, 67–69, 72–73, 76–77, and 79 by David Guyor and Marlena Toohey.

Photography on pages 17, 19, 22–25, 29–30, 34–36, 40–41, 43–56, 63–66, 70–71, 74–75, and 78 by David E. Richardson.

© May 1999

The Glass Press, Inc.
dba **Antique Publications**
P.O. Box 553 • Marietta, Ohio 45750

PB ISBN 1-57080-056-1
HB ISBN 1-57080-057-X

Contents

Dedication

My thanks go to all of you who have encouraged me to continue my research and also to those who have contributed your knowledge and information on pieces in my collection. My special thanks, once again, to my husband, John, sons Brian and Brandon, and my mother, Naomi, who continue to support and help me in my unrelenting quest, searching for that next piece of black glass that I don't have, and just can't live without!

Introduction

Trademarks and company stamps can offer valuable information toward attributing and identifying glass collectibles. The following figures represent some of the trademarks found on the black glass items illustrated in this book. The companies listed are grouped according to geographic location.

McKee

The **McKee Glass Company** of Jeannette, Pennsylvania manufactured a wide range of pressed, or imitation-cut, tableware. Its "Prescut" mark was used on these tableware lines after 1904. Another McKee mark that I have seen on glassware is similar to that shown here.

Fig. 1 Facsimile of trademark found on McKee's ebony circa 1950s.

L. E. Smith

The **L. E. Smith Glass Company** of Mt. Pleasant, Pennsylvania utilized two different trademarks that I have seen.

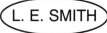

Figs. 2 & 3 Facsimile of markings found on glass made for and by L. E. Smith.

Boyd

Boyd's Crystal Art Glass of Cambridge, Ohio modified its own trademark to indicate different years of production.

Fig. 4 1978–83   *Fig. 5 1984–88*   *Fig. 6 1989–93*

Fig. 7 1994–98   *Fig. 8 1999–current*

Degenhart, Cambridge, Heisey

Degenhart's Crystal Art Glass (of Cambridge, Ohio), **Cambridge Glass**, and **Heisey Glass** (of Newark, Ohio) each utilized a single trademark to identify their own glassware.

Fig. 9 Degenhart   *Fig. 10 Cambridge*   *Fig. 11 Heisey*

Guernsey, Summit

The **Guernsey Glass Company** of Cambridge, Ohio marked its wares with a B in a triangle, including items made for the company by others such as Imperial Glass Corporation, Mosser Glass and Westmoreland Glass. Novelty items made by and for **Summit Art Glass** (Rootstown, Ohio) utilized V in a circle, after founders Russ and Joann Vogelsong.

Fig. 12 Guernsey Glass   *Fig. 13 Summit Art Glass*

Barnes, Hunter, Mosser

Items made by Mosser Glass Company (also of Cambridge, Ohio) for independent designers, such as **Edna Barnes** and **Vi Hunter**, carried their own special trademarks. Mosser marked its own wares with an M.

Figs. 14 Mosser Glass   *Figs. 15 & 16 Trademarks found on items made by Mosser Glass for Edna Barnes and Vi Hunter.*

Our Gang Collectors

RW *Fig. 17 Trademark appearing on items made for Our Gang Collectors by R. Wetzel Glass of Zanesville, Ohio and Quality Glass of Cambridge, Ohio.*

FENTON

The **Fenton Art Glass Company** employed a series of marks depending upon year of manufacture, beginning in 1970 with the Fenton oval. Until about 1973, the Fenton oval trademark appeared only in carnival and hobnail items. By

Fig. 18 1970s   *Fig. 19* 1980s   *Fig. 20* 1990s

1975, most items were marked. Beginning in 1983, Fenton utilized a script F in an oval to indicate glass made in molds that were purchased from other glass companies (with the exception of Verlys pieces).

Figs. 21 & 22 F in oval used 1983 forward to mark other companies' molds; new logo used 1984 forward on pieces that did not already have an older Fenton logo in mold.

IMPERIAL

The **Imperial Glass Corporation** of Bellaire, Ohio used a number of trademarks and logos on its numerous lines of glassware, only some of which are mentioned here.

Fig. 23 This split Imperial mark was first used in 1913.

Fig. 24 A similar trademark over the iron cross was used beginning in 1914, and appeared on much of the company's art glass.

Fig. 25 A common Imperial marks, this I over G appears mostly on milk glass and colored glass items.

Fig. 26 An L was added to the IG mark to denote glass made after Imperial was purchased by Lenox in 1977.

Fig. 27 An A was added before the LIG to make this mark, used after Arthur Lorch took over operations at Imperial, between the Lenox years and the early 1980s.

WESTMORELAND

The **Westmoreland Glass Company** (Grapeville, Pennsylvania) has a history of marks on its decorated glass tableware and novelty items. Westmoreland manufactured its own glassware, but other companies have obtained Westmoreland molds and are producing glass, in some cases, with the original trademark intact.

Fig. 28 The Keystone symbol first appeared on Westmoreland wares circa 1910. The mark was discontinued before the Depression era, but can still be found on 1970s reissues of earlier patterns.

Fig. 29 This common WG mark was used by Westmoreland from the 1940s until 1982.

Fig. 30 The circular mark was used from 1983 until the factory closed the following year

PLUM GLASS, ROSSO

Reproduction Westmoreland items have been found with two other trademarks, indicating that they were made in the original molds for **Plum Glass** and **Rosso's Wholesale Glass**. Rosso also employed an AB trademark, indicating glassware made in molds designed by Al Botson's Machine & Mold Company.

Fig. 31 Keystone mark used to indicate newer pieces made in the old Westmoreland mold for Plum Glass.

Fig. 32 Keystone mark used to indicate newer pieces made in the old Westmoreland mold for Rosso's Wholesale Glass.

Fig. 33 Trademark indicating glass made for Rosso in molds by Al Botson's Machine & Mold.

On the Covers

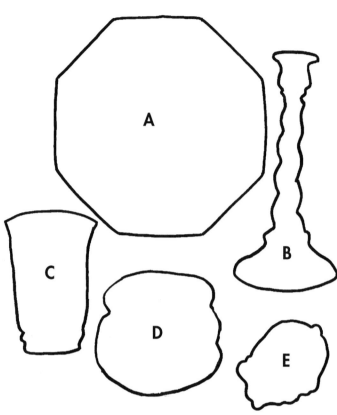

Front Cover

A. Cambridge Glass Company, octagonal platter, Ebony with silver decoration (see **Figure 173**).

B. H. Northwood Company, twisted candle-stick (see **Figure 601**).

C. Venetian flower vase with applied gold decoration (see **Figure 319**).

D. Fenton Art Glass Company, covered candy dish with Copper Rose decoration (see **Figure 161**).

E. Imperial Glass Corporation, Pig figurine from Heisey mold (see **Figure 282**).

Back Cover

F. Murano Glass, swirled bowl with white and black glass (see **Figure 316**).

G. Heart-shaped box with cover, used to hold cosmetics samples, unknown maker (refer to **Figure 474** in *Book 1*).

H. Cambridge Glass Company, cigarette box with intaglio decoration (see **Figure 136**).

I. Oneida Crystal, perfume bottle (**Figure 839**).

J. Miniature Seal (see **Figure 528**).

K. Pairpoint Glass Works, Starfish (**Figure 665**)

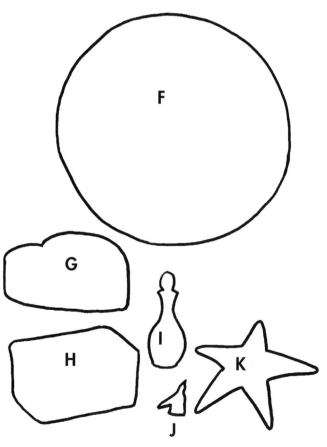

Captions

AVON, P. 18

Figures 1–22 were all purchased from Avon Collectibles. All glass bottles have plastic lids. Manufacturers of each piece are not known.

1. Chief Pontiac, black glass base, 6" high, 1976.

2. Eightball, $2^3/_4$" diameter, 1973.

3. Pot-bellied Stove, $4^3/_4$" high, 1970–71.

4. Super Shift (for automobile), black glass base, 7" high, 1978.

5. American Eagle, $6^3/_4$" high, 1973–75.

6. Miniature Schoolhouse Desk, black glass base, $3^1/_2$" wide, 1972–74.

7. Cat, 4" high, 1975–76.

8. Swinger Golf Bag, 7" high, 1969–71.

9. NFL decanter (decanter comes with different team logos) Denver Broncos, football cap, 6" high, 1976–77.

10. Zodiac bottle (comes with all Zodiac signs) Pisces, round cap, $4^3/_4$" high, 1975.

11. Paperclip on round base, $7^1/_4$" high, 1978–79.

12. Volkswagen, $5^3/_4$" long, 2" high, 1970–72.

13. Domino, $4^1/_4$" high, 1978–79.

14. Marine binoculars, silver-colored eyepiece, $6^1/_2$" high, 1973–74.

15. Skunk, $3^1/_2$" high, 1978–80.

16. Sitting Poodle bottle, $5^1/_4$" high, 1973.

17. Salt and pepper shakers, $6^1/_2$" high, 1969.

18. Electric charger (jalopy with red accents), 6" long, 3" high, 1970–72.

19. Mini Lamp, cauldron with daisy shade, $6^3/_4$" high, 1973–76.

20. Jeep, $5^1/_4$" long, $2^1/_2$" high, 1981–82.

21. Lotus jar with painted decoration, $6^1/_2$" high, 1974–75.

22. Microphone, $5^1/_2$" high, 1975–76.

BOTTLES, P. 19

23. Stretched triple bottle vase, $9^3/_4$" high, unknown maker, no marks.

24. Liquor bottle with Americana No. 2 portrait, copy of "The Alamo" by Lawrence Butcher, $9^1/_2$" high, for Kentucky Bourbon 1969.

25. Wine bottle, satin finish, 12" high, marked, made for Freixenet Negro, Spain 1985.

26. Soda bottle, $9^3/_4$" high, made by/for Mission Orange, bottom of bottle is marked "Mission Orange."

27. Soda bottle, $9^3/_4$" high, unknown maker, no markings.

28. Liquor decanter, American bald eagle, Bicentennial Collector's Edition, $9^3/_4$" high, for Fleischmann's 1976.

29. Poodle decanter, $15^3/_4$" high, unknown maker, no marks.

30A. Figure bottle, head only, black satin, $10^1/_2$" high, made by Inca Pisco of Lima, Peru circa 1970s.

30B. Figure bottle, black satin, 12" high, made by Inca Pisco of Lima, Peru circa 1970s.

31. Soda bottle with original cap and closure, marked "1958" on bottom, Anchor Hocking Glass Company of Lancaster, Ohio 1958.

32. Miniature figure bottle, black satin, $4^1/_4$" high, by Inca Pisco of Lima, Peru circa 1970s.

33. Miniature figure bottle, black satin, 4¼" high, by Inca Pisco of Lima, Peru circa 1970s.

34. Small figure bottle, black satin, 6½" high, by Inca Pisco of Lima, Peru circa 1970s.

35. Miniature figure bottle, black satin, 5" high, by Inca Pisco of Lima, Peru circa 1970s.

36. Miniature figure bottle, head only, black satin, 3½" high, by Inca Pisco of Lima, Peru circa 1970s.

37. Miniature figure bottle, head only, black satin, 4¼" high, by Inca Pisco of Lima, Peru circa 1970s.

BOYD'S CRYSTAL ART GLASS, P. 20

Figures 38–71 were made by Boyd's Crystal Art Glass of Cambridge, Ohio. Refer to page 4 for information on the company's trademarks.

38. Toothpick holder, Beaded Oval pattern, 2¾" high, Degenhart mold, marked with B in a diamond and 2 horizontal lines, 1991.

39. Duck ashtray, 7½" diameter, marked with B in a diamond and 2 horizontal lines, 1991.

40. Lamb salt, 2½" wide, marked with B in a diamond and 2 horizontal lines, 1991.

41. Zodiac ashtray, 7½" diameter, marked with B in a diamond and 2 horizontal lines, 1991.

42. Duck salt, 2½" wide, marked with B in a diamond and 2 horizontal lines, 1991.

43. Fish ashtray, 7½" diameter, marked with B in a diamond and 2 horizontal lines, 1991.

44. 2½" toothpick holder, Forget-Me-Not pattern, Degenhart mold, marked with B in a diamond and 2 horizontal lines, 1991.

45. Vanity mirror with handle, 8⅛" long, marked with B in a diamond and 2 horizontal lines, 1991.

46. 2-handled Basket toothpick holder, 2½" high, marked with B in a diamond and 2 horizontal lines, 1991.

47. Miniature spooner, part of 4-piece children's table set, Lamb design, 3" high, marked with B in a diamond and 2 horizontal lines, 1991.

48. Miniature covered butter, part of 4-piece children's table set, Lamb design and finial, 3" high, marked with B in a diamond and 2 horizontal lines, 1991.

49. Miniature covered sugar, part of 4-piece children's table set, Lamb design and finial, 4½" high, marked with B in a diamond and 2 horizontal lines, 1991.

50. Miniature creamer, part of 4-piece children's table set, Lamb design, 3" high, marked with B in a diamond and 2 horizontal lines, 1991.

51. Top Hat toothpick holder, 2½" high, marked with B in a diamond and 2 horizontal lines, 1991.

52. Tomahawk, 7⅛" long, marked with B in a diamond and 2 horizontal lines, 1991.

53. Caprice footed dresser box, Cambridge mold, 5" long, 2½" high, marked with B in a diamond and 2 horizontal lines, 1991.

54. Footed toothpick holder, Daisy & Button pattern, 2½" high, marked with B in a diamond and 2 horizontal lines, 1991.

55. "Patrick the Balloon Bear" figurine, 2⅛" high, marked with B in a diamond and 2 horizontal lines, 1991.

56. "Tucker Car" figurine, 3¾" long, marked with B in a diamond and 2 horizontal lines, 1991.

57. Tractor figurine, 2¾" wide, marked with B in a diamond, 1978–83.

58. "Artie Penguin" figurine, 3" high, marked with B in a diamond, 1984–88.

59. "Willy Mouse" figurine, 2" high, marked with B in a diamond and 2 horizontal lines, 1991.

60. Pressed Bird, 3" high, marked with B in a diamond and 2 horizontal lines, 1991.

61. Open salt, Star Drop pattern, 3⅛" diameter, marked with B in a diamond and 2 horizontal lines, 1989–93.

62. Dresser box, Candlewick pattern, Imperial mold, 5" long, 2½" high, marked with B in a diamond and 2 horizontal lines, 1991.

63. High boot, Daisy & Button pattern, 4⅛" high, marked with B in a diamond and 2 horizontal lines, 1991.

64. Elephant Head toothpick, 4¼" long, 2¼" high, marked with B in a diamond and 2 horizontal lines, 1991.

65. Skate boot, 4½" high, marked with B in a diamond and 2 horizontal lines, 1991.

66. Turkey covered dish, 5" long, 4½" high, ribbed base, marked with B in a diamond, 1984. This piece is a reproduction of the McKee turkey dish, originally made circa 1900. It was also reproduced by Kemple Glass of Kenova, West Virginia circa 1950, but not in black glass.

67. Company logo, diamond with raised B, 3¼" long, marked with B in a diamond and 2 horizontal lines, 1991.

68. Owl figurine, 3¾" high, marked with B in a diamond and 2 horizontal lines, 1991.

69. "Elizabeth Mini Doll" figurine, 2½" high, marked with B in a diamond and 2 horizontal lines, 1991.

70. "Pooch the Dog" figurine, 3" high, marked with B in a diamond, 1978–83.

71. Woodchuck figurine, 5½" high, marked with B in a diamond and 2 horizontal lines, 1991.

BOYD'S CRYSTAL ART GLASS AND OTHERS, PP. 21–22

Refer to pages 4–5 for information on each company's trademarks.

72. Rabbit covered dish, 6" long, 5½" high, marked with a B in a triangle, Guernsey Glass of Cambridge, Ohio 1967.

73. Hand ashtray, 5⅛" long, marked with B in a diamond, Boyd's Crystal Art Glass 1978–83.

74. Chick salt, 2½" wide, marked with B in a diamond, made in old Degenhart mold, Boyd's Crystal Art Glass 1984.

75. Rocky Horse, 3½" wide, marked with a B in a triangle, made by Imperial Glass Corporation, in an old Cambridge Glass Company mold for Guernsey Glass 1982.

76. Baby Shoe (toothpick holder), 2⅛" high, 2¾" long, marked with a B in a diamond, Boyd's Crystal Art Glass 1978–83.

77. Swan, 3½" long, marked with a B in a diamond, Boyd's Crystal Art Glass 1978–83.

78. "Pooch the Dog" figurine, 3" high, marked with B in a diamond and 2 horizontal lines, 1991.

79. "Kitten on a Pillow" figurine, 3½" high, marked with B in a diamond, Boyd's Crystal Art Glass 1978–83.

80. Indian Head toothpick holder, footed, 2½" high, marked with a B in a triangle, Guernsey Glass of Cambridge, Ohio 1982.

81. Mini Pitcher, Dogwood pattern, 2¼" high, marked with a B in a diamond, Boyd's Crystal Art Glass 1978–83.

82. Bird salt and pepper shakers, 3" high, marked with a B in a diamond, Boyd's Crystal Art Glass 1978–83.

83. Turkey covered dish, 5" long, 4½" high, ribbed base, marked with B in a diamond, Boyd's Crystal Art Glass 1984 (see notes for **Figure 66**.)

84–89. 6-piece "Boyd Special Train," each piece ranges from 2½" to 3½" long, marked with B in a diamond and horizontal line underneath, Boyd's Crystal Art Glass 1984.

90. Boyd Airplane, 4¼" long with "BOYD" across wing, marked with B in a diamond and horizontal line underneath, Boyd's Crystal Art Glass 1984.

91. Boyd Airplane, black satin, 4¼" long with "BOYD" across wing, marked with B in a diamond and horizontal line underneath, Boyd's Crystal Art Glass 1984.

92. "Scotty Dog" figurine, black satin, 4" long, JB Glass Company circa 1980s.

93. Owl bell, 4" high, marked with B in a diamond and line underneath, Boyd's Crystal Art Glass 1984.

94. "Debbie Duck" figurine, 3" high, marked with B in a diamond and 2 horizontal lines, Boyd's Crystal Art Glass 1984.

95. Duckling figurine, $1^{1}/_{2}$" high, marked with B in a diamond and 2 horizontal lines, Boyd's Crystal Art Glass 1984.

96. Duckling figurine, black satin, $1^{1}/_{2}$" high, marked with B in a diamond and 2 horizontal lines, Boyd's Crystal Art Glass 1984.

97. Colonial Man, "Christopher," $4^{1}/_{4}$" high, marked with B in a diamond and line underneath, Boyd's Crystal Art Glass 1984.

98. Colonial Doll, "Xenia," 4" high, marked with B in a diamond and line underneath, Boyd's Crystal Art Glass 1984.

99. "Teddy Tugboat," 3" long, marked with B in a diamond and a line underneath, Boyd's Crystal Art Glass 1984.

100. Bunny Salt, $2^{1}/_{2}$" wide, marked with B in a diamond and a line underneath, Boyd's Crystal Art Glass 1984.

101. Gypsy Pot toothpick holder, $2^{1}/_{2}$" high, marked with B in a diamond and line underneath, Boyd's Crystal Art Glass 1984.

102. "Little Luck Unicorn," 3" high, marked with B in a diamond and 2 horizontal lines, Boyd's Crystal Art Glass 1991.

103. 2-piece covered candy dish, Rooster with milk glass head, 9" high, marked with keystone, Rosso's Wholesale Glass circa 1980s.

104. Rooster toothpick holder, footed, $4^{1}/_{2}$" wide, marked with B in a diamond, Boyd's Crystal Art Glass 1978–83.

105. Lion Cub figurine, $2^{1}/_{2}$" high, marked with B in a diamond and 3 lines, Boyd's Crystal Art Glass 1994.

106. Cat covered dish, 5" wide with ribbed base, Westmoreland mold, marked with keystone R, Rosso's Wholesale Glass circa 1980s.

107. Mini Jenny Doll, $2^{1}/_{8}$" high, marked with H, for Vi Hunter (by Mosser Glass) circa 1980.

108. Jenny Doll, $4^{1}/_{2}$" high, marked with H, for Vi Hunter (by Mosser Glass) circa 1980.

109. Scottie Dog figurine, 2" high, L. E. Smith Glass Company circa pre-1960s.

110. Bulldog doorstop with red leather collar, weighs $7^{1}/_{2}$ pounds, $8^{1}/_{2}$" high, marked with V in a circle, Summit Art Glass circa 1990s.

111. Figural fish, black satin with white enamel decoration, $3^{3}/_{4}$" high, with paper label, made in Taiwan 1992.

112. Tyrannosaurus Rex figurine, $4^{1}/_{2}$" high, marked with B in a diamond and 2 horizontal lines, Boyd's Crystal Art Glass 1989–93.

113. Swan dish, handblown, 9" long, no markings, made in Mexico circa 1970s.

114. Figural fish, black satin with white enamel decoration, 4" high, with paper label, made in Taiwan 1992.

115. Elephant egg cup, $2^{3}/_{4}$" high, no markings, unknown maker circa 1980s.

116. Cat salt, $2^{1}/_{2}$" wide, signed M for Mosser Glass circa 1990s.

117. Poodle figurine, $5^{1}/_{2}$" high to top of head, signed Baccarat, made in France, Baccarat Crystal 1988.

118. Horse figurine, $3^{3}/_{4}$" high to top of head, signed Baccarat, made in France, Baccarat Crystal 1988.

119. Footed eye cup, $2^{1}/_{2}$" high, no markings, Rosso's Wholesale Glass circa 1980s.

120. Turtle paperweight, 4" long, End-of-Day (slag), no markings, unknown maker circa 1920s–30s.

121. Bulldog Head toothpick holder, black carnival, $3^{1}/_{2}$" wide, unknown maker.

122. 5¼" handblown figural bird, unknown maker circa 1990s.

123. 4¼" handblown figural snail, unknown maker circa 1990s.

124. 3¾" handblown rabbit figurine, unknown maker circa 1990s.

125. Miniature basket, 4" wide, with paper label, made in Taiwan circa 1990s.

126. Daisy & Button Top Hat, 2½" high, marked with B in a diamond and 2 horizontal lines, Boyd's Crystal Art Glass 1989–93.

127. Cat slipper, 6¼" long, 2¾" high, marked "Made in Taiwan" circa 1980s.

128. Daisy & Button slipper, 5¼" long, 2¼" high, no markings, made for L. G. Wright Glass Company circa 1980s.

129. High boot, Daisy & Button pattern, 4¾" high, made in Taiwan.

130. "Bottoms Up" 3½" cocktail tumbler and 4" coaster, woman lying over dome of cup, similar to the old McKee mold (c. 1932) but made by Rosso's Wholesale Glass 1998.

131. No. 9144 ring holder, Fine Cut & Block pattern, 3" wide, Fenton logo, circa 1980s.

132. Heart paperweight, cased crystal over black, 3½" long, no markings, unknown maker.

133. Daisy & Button slipper, 6" long, 2½" high, unknown maker circa 1980s.

134. Bow slipper, 4¾" long, 2¾" high, unknown maker circa 1990s.

CAMBRIDGE AND FOSTORIA, P. 23

Both the Cambridge Glass and Fostoria Glass companies marketed their black wares as Ebony. Cambridge began making this color in 1916, and continued periodically until 1954. Fostoria manufactured Ebony from 1924–41, during the 1950s, and as recently as 1982.

135. Ashtray with silver overlay, 5" diameter, Cambridge Glass Company circa 1930s.

136. No. 607 cigarette box with intaglio dog on lid, 5" long, Cambridge Glass Company circa 1920s–30s.

137. No. 3400 footed bowl, 12" wide, Cambridge Glass Company circa 1920s–30s.

138. No. 1216 candelabrum shown with crystal flower holders, Leaf or Everglades line, 5½" high, 11" high to top of crystal, Cambridge Glass 1933–45.

139. No. 3400 wine, 2 oz. glass in Farberware holder, marked Farberware, Cambridge Glass Company circa 1940s.

140. No. 2430 vase, Diadem pattern, 8" high, Fostoria Glass Company 1929–33.

141. 8 oz. champagne, milk glass on black stem, marked Fostoria Glass Company.

142. Prism sign with "Cambridge Glass" in Old English letters, 2½" long.

143. Octagonal platter with silver decoration, 10¼" wide, Cambridge Glass Company circa 1920s–40s.

144. No. 2395 candlestick with scroll, 3½" high, Fostoria Glass Company 1928.

145. Oval centerpiece bowl with scroll, part of No. 2395 line, 13½" long, Fostoria Glass Company 1928.

146. No. 2395½ candlestick with scroll, 5" high, Fostoria Glass Company 1928.

MADE IN CHINA, P. 24

147. Lotus bowl, 9½" wide, with paper label, manufactured 1985–90.

148. Lotus bowl, 6¼" wide, with paper label, manufactured 1985–90.

149. Lotus bowl, 11¾" diameter, with paper label, manufactured 1985–90.

150. 6 oz. wine glass, with label, circa 1990s.

151. 8 oz. champagne glass, with label, made by Gibson circa 1990s.

152. 12 oz. water glass, with paper label, made by PBG circa 1990s.

153. 16 oz. crystal iced tea mug with black handle, with paper label, circa 1990s.

154. 8" vase, with paper label, circa 1990s.

155. Leaf bowl, $8^3/_4$" long, with paper label, circa 1990s.

156. Leaf bowl, 6" long, with paper label, circa 1990s.

157. Candleholder vase (can be turned upside down to use as vase), $4^1/_2$" diameter, with paper label, circa 1990s.

158. Candleholder, $2^1/_4$" high, with paper label, circa 1990s.

159. Soy sauce jar, 3" high, marked "Wing Fung Hong," circa 1990s.

Fenton Art Glass Company, pp. 25–26

Fenton also called its black glass Ebony beginning in 1916, and then again during the 1920s and '30s. Manufactured off and on throughout the following decades, black glass has been made as recently as the mid-1990s. Refer to pages 5–6 for information on the company's trademarks.

160. No. 7523 rolled rim bowl, handpainted Copper Rose decoration, $9^3/_4$" diameter, Fenton logo and label, 1989–91.

161. No. 6080 covered candy dish, handpainted Copper Rose decoration, $5^1/_2$" wide, $4^1/_2$" high, Fenton logo and label, 1989–91.

162. No. 7696 ruffled vase, handpainted Copper Rose decoration, $7^1/_2$" high, Fenton logo and label, 1989–91.

163. No. 7550 vase, $6^1/_2$" high, Fenton logo, circa 1990s.

164. No. 847 fan vase, 6" high, 1932.

165. Sweet pea vase with flattened rim, 5" high, $3^1/_2$" wide, no markings. While this vase has been attributed to Fenton, and bears some resemblance to the Top Hat, it is not a Fenton piece.

166. Sweet pea vase with flattened rim, $4^1/_2$" high, no markings. While this vase has been attributed to Fenton, and bears some resemblance to the Top Hat, it is not a Fenton piece.

167. No. 2757 vase, handpainted decoration, 5" high, Fenton logo and label, 1995. This decoration was first offered as part of the 1994 Family Signature Series, and was most likely continued the following year.

168. No. 2759 rose bowl, handpainted decoration, $3^1/_2$" wide, Fenton logo and label, 1995. This decoration was first offered as part of the 1994 Family Signature Series, and was most likely continued the following year.

169. No. 5253 Unicorn, handpainted decoration, 5" high, has Fenton logo and signature, from the 1994 Family Signature Series.

170. No. 5226 Fox, handpainted decoration, $4^3/_4$" high, Fenton logo, 1996. This decoration was first offered as part of the 1994 Family Signature Series.

171. No. 5145 Collectible Egg paperweight, handpainted decoration, $3^1/_2$" high, Fenton logo, 1995.

172. No. 5168 Owl figurine, 3" high, Fenton label, circa 1980s.

173. No. 1992 Daisy & Button hat, $2^1/_2$" high, Fenton logo, circa 1980s.

174. No. 6006 salt and pepper shakers, handpainted Copper Rose decoration, $2^1/_2$" high, marked with Fenton logo, made for QVC 1996.

175. 4 oz. glass, circa 1930s.

176. No. 2931 handpainted Secret Slipper, 5" long, 3" high, with Fenton logo, made for QVC 1996.

177. No. 107 tulip vase, $6^1/_2$" high, 1933.

178. No. 9266 Bow & Drape bell, handpainted flowers, $6^3/_4$" high, Fenton logo, circa 1990s.

179. No. 5178 Pelican ashtray, $5^1/_2$" long, $4^1/_2$"

high, with label, 1997. This piece was made from a Verlys mold and sold through the FAGCA. Fenton acquired some retired Verlys molds from the Holophane Co. in Newark, Ohio in 1966.

180. No. 1533 crimped compote, dolphin handles and silver decoration, 6" wide, circa 1930s. Rare.

181. Rolled edge vase, Butterfly and Berry pattern, footed, 5" high, 1916. Rare.

182. Owl figurine, handpainted, $5^1/_2$" high on wooden stand, Fenton logo and label, 1996.

183. No. 7651 cylinder vase, Sophisticated Ladies line, sandcarved, $10^3/_4$" high, has Fenton label, 1982.

184. No. 1902 bell, 4" high, Fenton label, 1981.

185. No. 7655 sphere vase, Sophisticated Ladies line, sandcarved, 10" high, has Fenton label 1982.

186. No. 5180 2-piece "Wise Owl Decision Maker," $3^3/_4$" high, Fenton logo, 1969–72.

187. No. 7561 vase, Sophisticated Ladies line, sandcarved, $10^3/_4$" high, Fenton label, 1982.

188. Bell, $6^3/_4$" high, Fenton label, 1986–87.

189. Swirl vase, 8" high, Fenton logo, circa 1980s.

190. No. 3602BW salt and pepper shakers in milk and black glass, $3^1/_8$" high, Fenton logo, 1962–65.

191. No. 5197 Happiness Bird, handpainted Copper Rose decoration, $5^1/_2$" long (to tip of tail), Fenton F logo and label, 1989–91.

192. No. 9266 Bow & Drape bell, handpainted Copper Rose decoration, 4" high, Fenton logo, 1989–91.

193. No. 8691 alarm clock, handpainted Copper Rose decoration, 4" high, Fenton logo, 1989–91.

194. No. 6761 Empress bell, handpainted Copper Rose decoration, $6^3/_4$" high, Fenton logo, 1989–91.

195. No. C5165 Cat figurine, handpainted Copper Rose decoration, $3^1/_2$" high, Fenton logo, 1989–91.

196. No. 5168 Owl figurine, 3" high, Fenton label, circa 1980s.

197. No. 5148 Mouse figurine, 3" high, Fenton logo, 1986.

198. No. 5214 Scottie Dog figurine, 3" high, Fenton logo, 1986.

199. No. 5160 Fawn figurine, $3^3/_4$" high, Fenton logo, 1986.

200. No. 5158 Elephant figurine, $3^3/_4$" high, Fenton logo, 1986.

201. No. 5119 Kitten figurine, $4^1/_4$" long, Fenton logo, 1986.

202. No. 5147 Mallard Duck, $5^1/_4$" high, Fenton logo, 1986.

203. No. 5151 sitting Bear Cub, $3^1/_2$" high, Fenton logo, circa 1980s.

204. No. 5100 Praying Girl, $3^3/_4$" high, Fenton label, circa 1970s.

205. No. 5100 Praying Boy, $3^3/_4$" high, Fenton label, circa 1970s.

206. Marquis vase, $7^1/_2$" high, circa 1980s.

207. No. 1991 Daisy & Button top hat, $2^1/_2$" high, Fenton logo, circa 1980s.

208. Miniature basket, Peachcrest handle and petticoat, 4" high, 1986.

209. No. 8200 heart-shaped covered dish, black carnival, $8^3/_4$" long, $7^1/_2$" wide, circa 1970s. This piece was made from a Verlys mold. Fenton acquired some retired Verlys molds from the Holophane Company in Newark, Ohio in 1966.

210. No. 8740 Iceberg, 6" wide, circa 1980s.

211. No. 9144 ring holder, Fine Cut & Block pattern, 3" wide, Fenton logo, circa 1990s.

212. Oval footed bowl, 8$\frac{1}{2}$" long, 3" high, made from an Imperial Glass mold, marked with LIG, circa 1980s.

Fenton, Indiana and Summit, p. 27

The Indiana Glass Company of Dunkirk (IN) manufactured black glass periodically from the 1970s through the 1980s. In 1961 it became a subsidiary of Lancaster Colony Corporation. Summit Art Glass of Ravenna, Ohio made black glass in 1993.

213. No. 5177 Alley Cat, 11$\frac{3}{4}$" high, Fenton Art Glass Company circa 1970.

214. 8 oz. goblet, Imperial's Candlewick pattern, Fenton Art Glass Company 1969. Purchased off the assembly line that year, this piece was made from an Imperial Glass mold, though it must have been an experimental item as it never appeared in Fenton catalogs.

215. No. 7630 Aurora basket, handpainted Copper Rose decoration, 6" high, Fenton logo, 1989–91.

216. No. 4429 footed compote, Thumbprint pattern, 5$\frac{1}{2}$" high, Fenton label, 1968–74.

217. No. 4425 footed vase, Thumbprint pattern, 9$\frac{3}{4}$" high, Fenton label, circa 1980s.

218. 12 oz. souvenir mug, marked "Dallas," Indiana Glass Company circa 1980s–90s.

219. Stemmed candleholder, 4$\frac{1}{2}$" high, with label, Indiana Glass Co. circa 1980s–90s.

220. Candleholder, 2$\frac{1}{2}$" high, with label, Indiana Glass Company circa 1980s–90s.

221. Cat candleholder, 5" long, 2$\frac{3}{4}$" high, with label, Indiana Glass Co. circa 1990s.

222. 2 oz. shot glass, scenic decal, with label, Indiana Glass Company circa 1990s. This type of shot glass has been made by a dozen or more glass companies. The glasses are similar in value unless they denote special events, such as the 1893 World's Fair.

223. Raised candlestick, 6$\frac{1}{2}$" high, with label, Indiana Glass Company circa 1990s.

224. Covered butter dish, Old Quilt pattern, 7$\frac{1}{4}$"

wide, marked with WG, made in the original Westmoreland mold by Summit Art Glass, 1993.

225. Covered sugar, Old Quilt pattern, 6$\frac{1}{2}$" high, marked WG, made in the original Westmoreland mold by Summit Art Glass, 1993.

226. Creamer, Old Quilt pattern, 4" high, marked with WG, made in the original Westmoreland mold by Summit Art Glass, 1993.

227. Miniature dish, chicken pattern, 4" long, Summit Art Glass 1993.

Foreign and Imported, pp. 28–29

228. Flower pot, 5$\frac{1}{2}$" wide, 3$\frac{1}{2}$" high, circa 1990s.

229. Round platter, 18$\frac{3}{4}$" diameter, circa 1990s.

230. Candy dish, 5$\frac{1}{2}$" wide, 3$\frac{1}{2}$" high, with label, Indiana Glass Company circa 1990s.

231. Hanging ball ornament, handblown, 4$\frac{1}{2}$" high, with label, made in Italy circa 1980s.

232. Heart vase, lead crystal, 3$\frac{1}{2}$" high, with label, made by Svend Jensen in Brazil 1991.

233. Jewel box, handpainted black satin, 5" long, 3$\frac{1}{2}$" high, marked "Taiwan" circa 1980s.

234. 2" napkin ring with multicolored glass swirls, with label, made in India circa 1980s.

235. Desk clock, 3" high, with label, made in West Germany circa 1980s.

236. Candy dish, 7" long, with label, made in Brazil circa 1980s.

237. Mannequin head, 11" high, with label, made in Spain circa 1990s.

238. Ram figurine, 5$\frac{1}{2}$" long, with label, made by Langham Glass in England 1992.

239. Grapes liquor decanter, black satin, 13" long, with label, made in Denmark circa 1980s.

240. 12 oz. water goblet, with label, made in China circa 1990s.

241. Mannequin head, 10" high, made in Spain circa 1980s.

242. Cigar humidor, 5¼" high, probably had a chrome lid originally, marked "Made in Hong Kong."

243. Vase, handpainted decoration, 7" high.

244. Art vase, free form, 12" high, with label, made in Poland 1996.

245. Art vase, free form, 10" high, with label, made in Poland 1996.

246. Candlestick, 6" high, unmarked circa 1990s.

247. Flower frog, black satin, 3¾" diameter, no markings circa 1930s–40s.

248. Flower frog, 2½" diameter, marked "Patent Applied for April 11, 1916."

248A. Swizzle stick with musical clef, 6" long, made in Taiwan circa 1980s.

248B. Swizzle stick with single die, 8" long, made in Taiwan circa 1980s.

248C. Swizzle stick with Scottie dog, 7½" long, made in Taiwan circa 1980s.

249. Flower frog, 3" diameter, no markings, circa 1930s–40s.

249A. Swizzle stick with top hat, 6" long, made in Taiwan circa 1980s.

249B. Swizzle stick with penguin, 7½" long, made in Taiwan circa 1990s.

249C. Swizzle stick with bow tie, 6" long, made in Taiwan circa 1980s.

250. Art vase, free form, 6½" high, with label, made in Poland 1996.

251. Punch ladle, handblown, 12" long, no markings, made in U. S. A.

252. Swizzle stick, 4¾" long, no markings.

253. Flower frog with raised floral design, 4½" diameter, Greensburg Glass Works circa

1930s. Chartered in 1889, the Greensburg Glass Company (first of Harrisburg then of East Greensburg, Pennsylvania) joined the National in 1899. It was sold to the Standard Glass Company in 1900, then purchased by L. E. Smith in 1920, where it operated as Greensburg Glass Works during the 1920s and 1930s.

253A. Swizzle stick, 7½" long, no markings.

253B. Swizzle stick, 5" long, marked "Buffalo Statler Hotel, Brooklyn."

253C. Swizzle stick, 7½" long, marked "Buffalo Statler Hotel, Brooklyn."

253D. Swizzle stick, 6¼" long, no markings.

253E. Swizzle stick with cherry, 6½" long, with label, made in Taiwan circa 1990s.

253F. Swizzle stick, 4¾" long, no markings.

254. Flower frog with raised floral design, 4½" diameter, Greensburg Glass Works circa 1930s (see notes for **Figure 253**).

255. Flower frog, 4¾" long, no markings circa 1930s.

256. Candy dish, black cut to crystal, 6" diameter, with label, made in Czechoslovakia circa 1990s.

257. Drink caddy with chrome holder and Bake-O-Lite handle, 5½" high, 4" wide, no markings circa 1930s.

258. Calligraphy pen, 8¾" long, with label, Murano Glass, made in Italy 1996.

259. Fisherman's ball (used to float fishing nets in the water), 6" diameter, unmarked.

260. 8 oz. rocks glass, handpainted Russian design, Libbey Glass Company of Dallas, Texas 1996.

261. Footed candy dish, 6" wide, no markings.

262. No. 151 square ashtray, 3½" wide, Cambridge Glass Company 1922.

(CONTINUED ON PAGE 81)

Notes on the Color Pages

This section of the book is devoted to the identification of over 1100 black glass items. The color photographs on pages 18–80 feature black glass items taken from my own collection for the express purpose of illustrating this book.

Each item has been assigned a figure number for identification in the Captions section (beginning on page 7). Where known, I have given a description of the item to include its shape, size, pattern or design, maker, country of origin, and date of manufacture. Pieces shown range from old to new, so the amount of information will vary from caption to caption. The figure number can also be used to locate a current price in the 1999 Value Guide (pages 123–127).

90-232

(90-223 Clea

90-227

90-220

90-234

90-226

(90-235 Black)

90-230

84-04

About the Author

It has been ten years since my first book on black glass was published! In that time, I have received hundreds of letters and phone calls from collectors who were glad to finally have some reference to their own unique collections of black glass. While they were thrilled to have this information, I was also informed it was still not enough.

After my first book came out, not only did many black glass collectors begin to surface, but so did some of the more beautiful and rare pieces, which are now highly sought after. The first book also encouraged collectors of other colors in glassware to realize the beauty and collectability of the amazing "black glass."

In the following pages, you will see I have included an additional 1,100 plus pieces of glassware from my own collection, to help you identify and date your own pieces. Please forgive the few duplicate items shown. The pictures were taken at different times, and a few pieces snuck in for a second appearance!

There are still unknown quantities and pieces of black glass hiding out there. Between my first book—*A Collector's Guide to Black Glass*—and the current one, you should certainly have a better idea of what is available to the avid collector. You just have to search it out!

Items shown are of all ages and origins, dating from pre-1900 to the day before we took these photographs, in March 1998. Although the older pieces are sometimes more enticing to many collectors, even the newest of items has become extremely collectable. So few pieces are made in black glass. When companies finally get around to making it, those pieces are snatched up and disappear as quickly as they appeared.

Please continue to write, as it has always been a pleasure to hear your stories and add your knowledge of black glass to my own. Enjoy the treasures you find in the following pages!

Avon

1   2   3   4   5   6   7   8

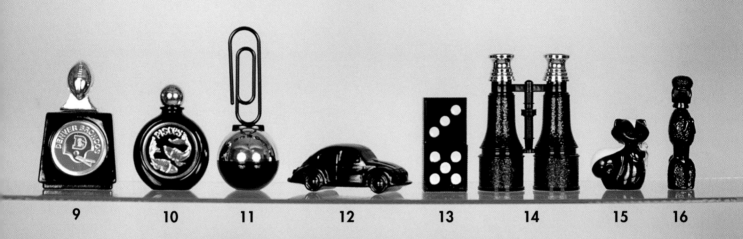

9   10   11   12   13   14   15   16

17   18   19   20   21   22

Bottles

23

24

25

26

27

28

29

30A

30B

31

32

33

34

35

36

37

Boyd

38 39 40 41 42 43 44

45 46 47 48 49 50 51 52

53 54 55 56 57 58 59 60 61 62

63 64 65 66 67 68 69 70 71

Boyd and Others

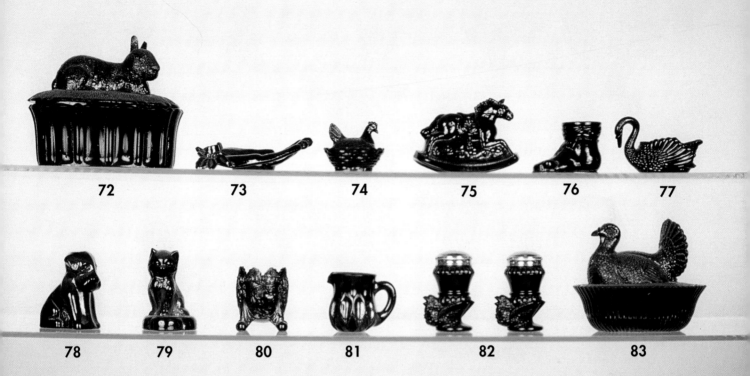

72   73   74   75   76   77

78   79   80   81   82   83

84   85   86   87   88   89   90   91

92   93   94   95   96   97   98   99   100   101   102

Boyd and Others

103

104

105

106

107

108 109

110

111

112

113

114

115

116

117

118

119

120

121

122

123

124

125

126

127

128

129

130

131

132

133

134

Cambridge

135

136

137

138

Fostoria

142

143

139

140

141

144

145

146

China

147   148   149

150   151   152   153   154

157

159

155   156   158

Fenton

160   161   162   163   164

165   166   167   168   169   170

171   172   173   174   175   176

177   178   179   180   181   182

Fenton

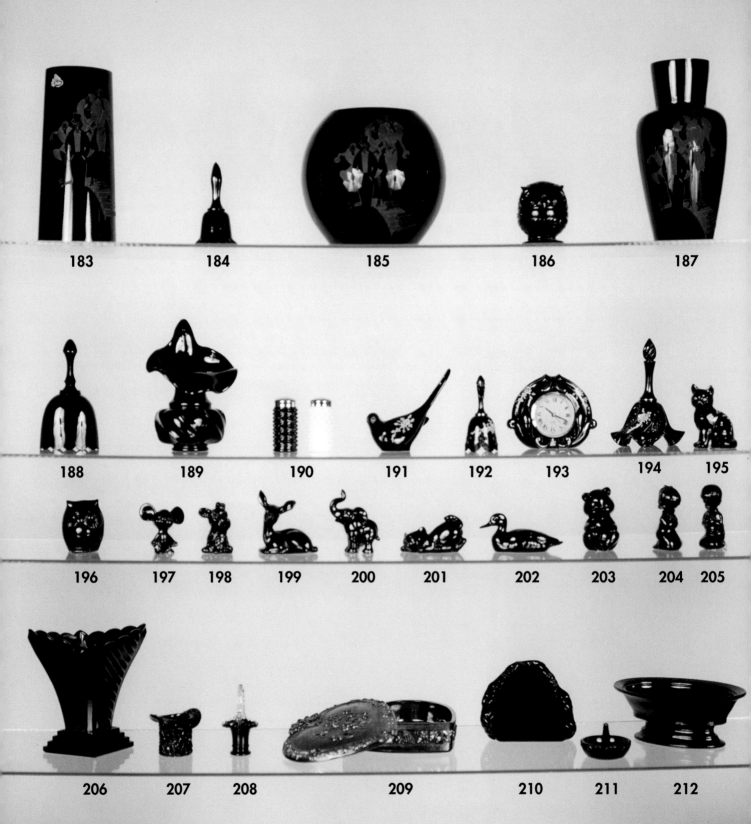

183   184   185   186   187

188   189   190   191   192   193   194   195

196   197   198   199   200   201   202   203   204   205

206   207   208   209   210   211   212

Fenton, Indiana
and Summit

213   214   215   216   217

218   219   220   221   222   223

224   225   226   227

Foreign and Imported

INDIANA GLASS

228

229

230

231

232

233

234

235

236

237

238

239

240

Foreign and Imported

241

242

243

244

245

AMERICAN

246

247

248

249

250

251

252

253

A

B

C

D

E

F

GREENSBURG GLASS

254

255

256

LIBBEY GLASS

257

258

259

260

261

262

263

264

265

CAMBRIDGE

FOSTORIA

29

Imperial

266

267

268

269   270   269   271

272

273

274

275

276

277

INDIANA GLASS **278**

Imperial
and Others

279   280   281   282   283

284   285   286

Italy

287 288 289 290 291 292

293 294 295 296

Italy

297   298   299   300   301   302   303

304   305   306   307   308   309   310

311   312   313   312   314

Italy

315

316

317

318

319

320

321

322

323

324 set

325

Jewelry

326

329

328

327

A

B

C

330 331

D

E

F

332

G

H

I

J

K

L

333

M

N

O

334 335

P

Q

R

S

T

336

337

338

339

341

342

343

340

344

345

346

Jewelry

347 348 349 350 351 352

353 354 355 356 357

358 359 360 361 362 363 364 367 368 369

361 365 366 370 371

372 373 374

375

376 377 378 379 380

Kitchenware

381

382

383

384

385

384

386

387

388

387

389

390

391

392 set

393

394

395

Kitchenware

396   397   398   399   400   401

402   403   404

405   406   407

Kitchenware

408   409   410   411   412   413   414

415   416   417   418

419   420   421   422

Kitchenware

423 424 425 426 427 428

429 430 431 432 433 434

435 436 437 438 439 440

441 442 443 444 445 446 447

448 449 450 451 452 453 454 455 456

40

Lamps

457

458

459

460

461

L. E. Smith
and Others

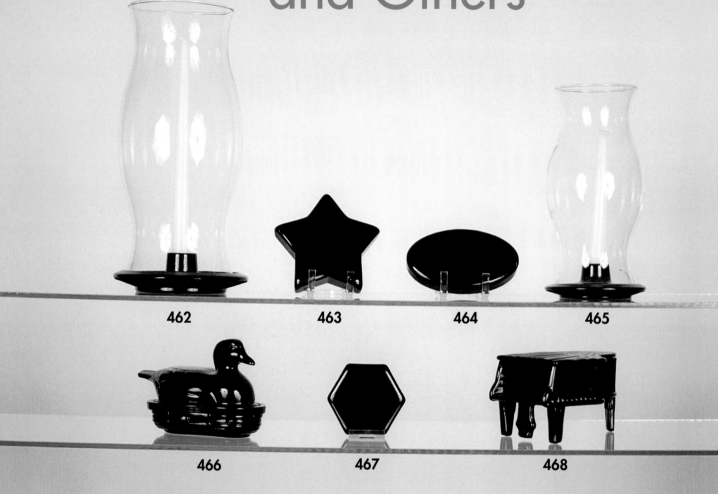

462   463   464   465

466   467   468

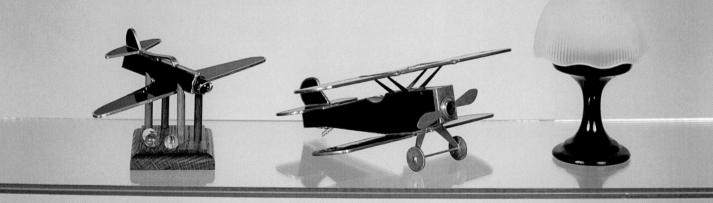

469   470   471

L. E. Smith and Others

472　　　　473　　　　474　　　　475

476　　　　477　　　　478　　　　477

479　　　　480　　　　481

L. E. Smith and McKee

482   483   484   485

486   487   488

489   490   491   493

492

Luncheon Sets

494   495A   495B   496A   496B   497   498

499   500A   500B   501A   501B   502

503   504A   504B   505A   505B   506

Luncheon Sets

507   508A   508B   509   510   511

512   513A   513B   514A   514B   515

516   517A   517B   518

Miniatures

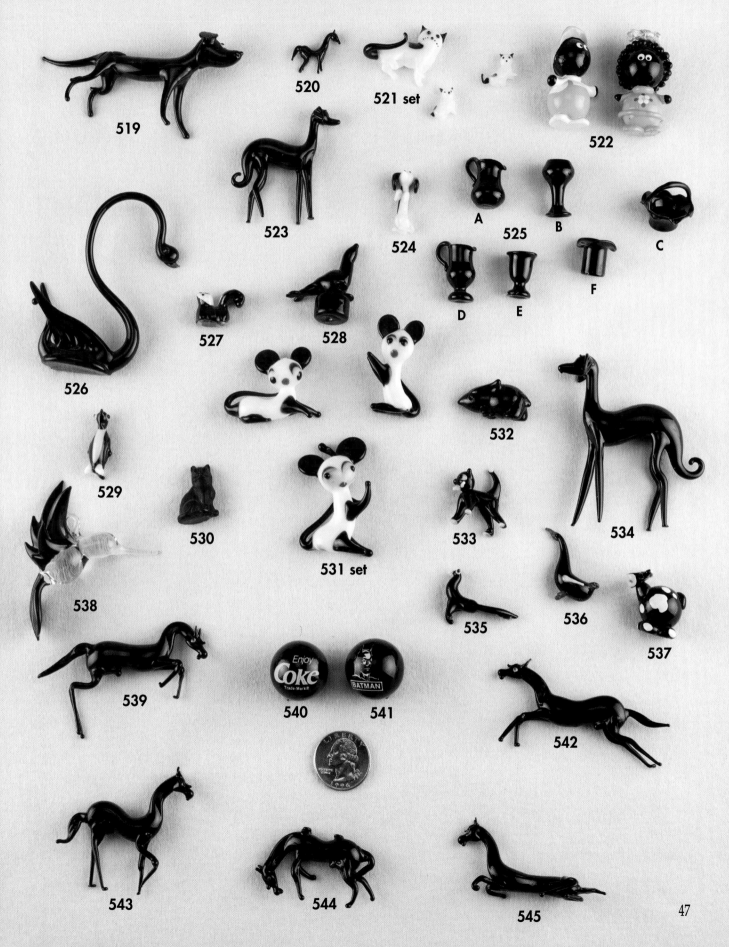

519

520

521 set

522

523

A

525

B

C

524

D

E

F

526

527

528

529

530

531 set

532

533

534

535

536

537

538

539

Enjoy Coke Trade-Mark®

540

BATMAN

541

542

543

544

545

47

Miscellany

546

547

548

547

549

550

551

552   553   554

555

556

557

558

559

560

Miscellany

561

562

563

564

565

Watermark Detector
DIRECTIONS FOR USE
Place the Stamp face down on the
black tray. Pour in enough Benzine
to cover the Stamp; the Watermark
will then be instantly revealed.

Benzine will not harm the most
delicate Stamp or affect either its
gum or color.

566

567

568

569

570

571

572

573

574

575

576

577

578

579

580

581

582

583

584

585

586

587

Miscellany

588

589 590

591

592

593

594

595 596

Miscellany

597

598

599

600

601

602

601

603

604

605

606

607

608

609

610

611

612

613

614

615

616

Miscellany

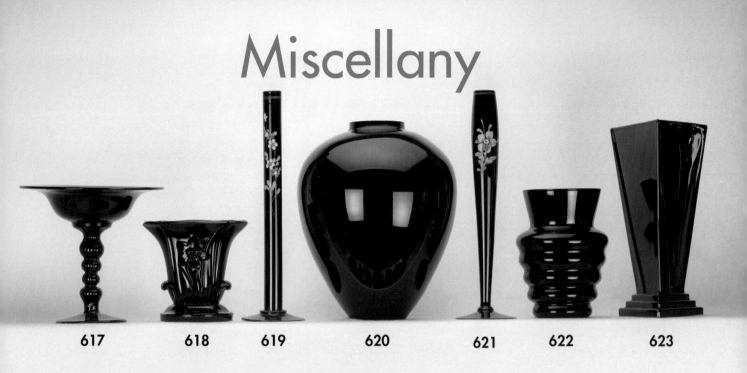

617   618   619   620   621   622   623

624   625   626   627   628

629   632   630   631   633   634   635   636   637   638   639

Miscellany

640   641A   641B   642   643   644   645

646   647   648   649   650

651   652   653   654 pair

Miscellany

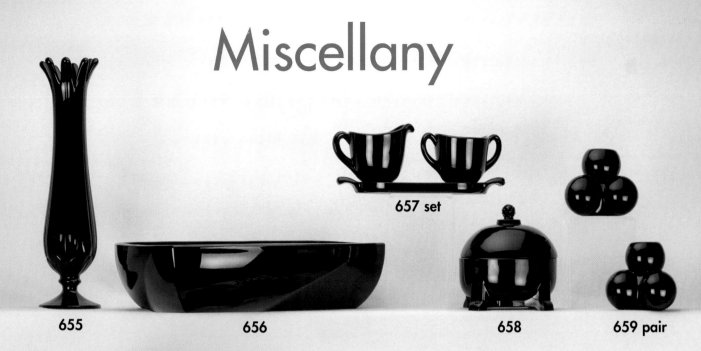

655

656

657 set

658

659 pair

660

661A

661B

662

663

664

665

666

Miscellany

667   668   669   670   671

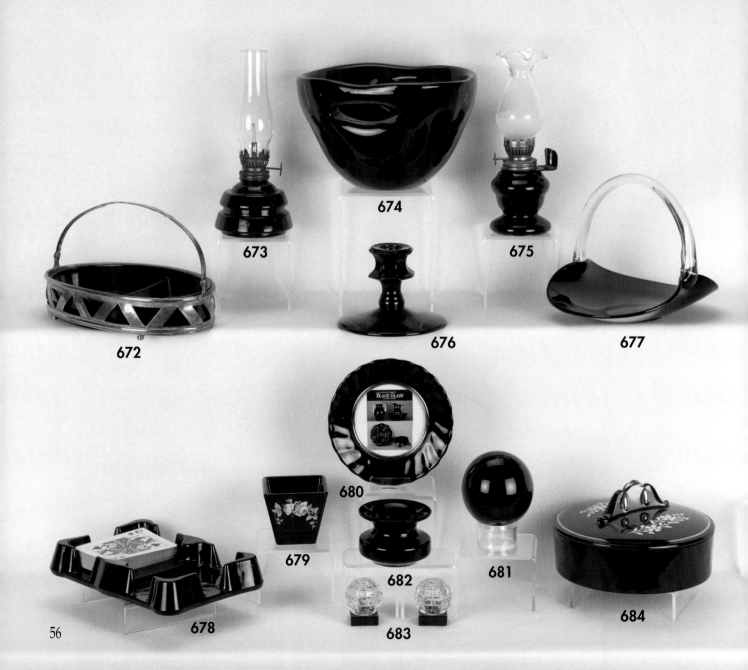

672   673   674   675   676   677

678   679   680   681   682   683   684

Miscellany

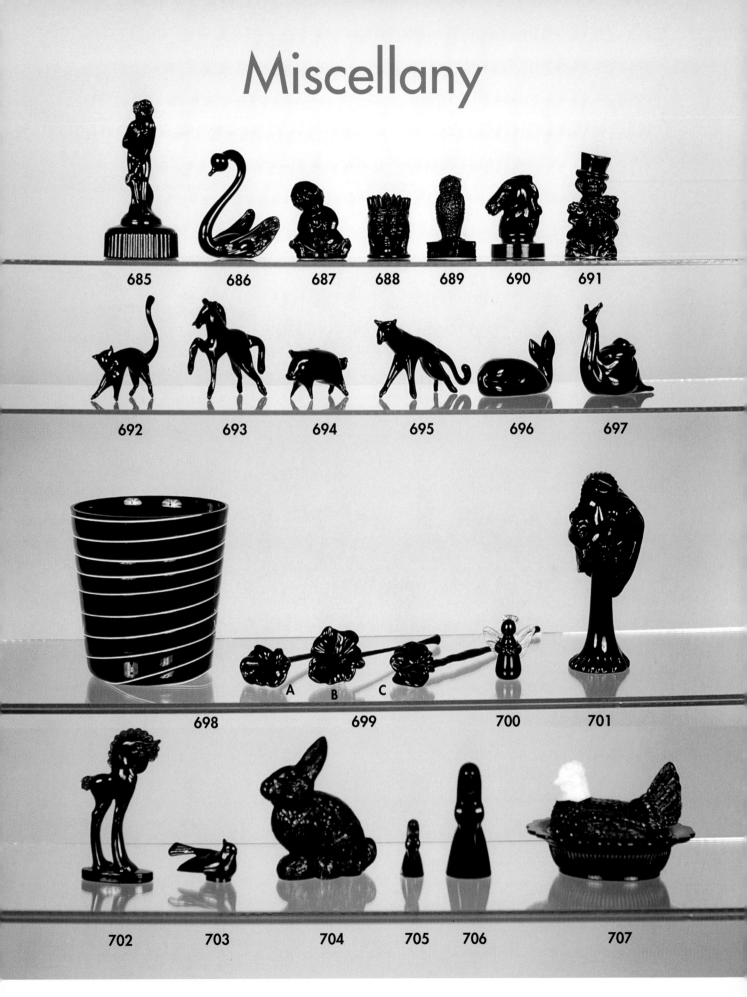

685 686 687 688 689 690 691

692 693 694 695 696 697

698 699 700 701

A B C

702 703 704 705 706 707

Miscellany

708 709 710 711 712 713 714 715 716 717

718 719 718 720 721 722 723

724 725 726 727 728 729 730 731 732

733 734 735 736 737 738 735 739

Mosser and Others

| 740 | 741 | 742 | 743 | 744 | 745 |

| 746 | 747 | 748 | 749 | 750 | 751 | 752 |

| 753 | 754 | 755 | 756 | 757 |

| 758 | 759 | 760 | 761 | 762 | 763 | 764 |

| 765 | 766 | 767 | 766 | 768 |

Oneida and Others

769 pair   770   771   772   773   774

775   776   777   778   779   780   781

782   783   784   785A   785B   786A   786B   787A   787B

Perfumes

788 789 790 791 792 793 794 795

796 797 798 799 800 801 802 803 804

805 806 807 808 809

810

Perfumes

811   812   813   814   815   816

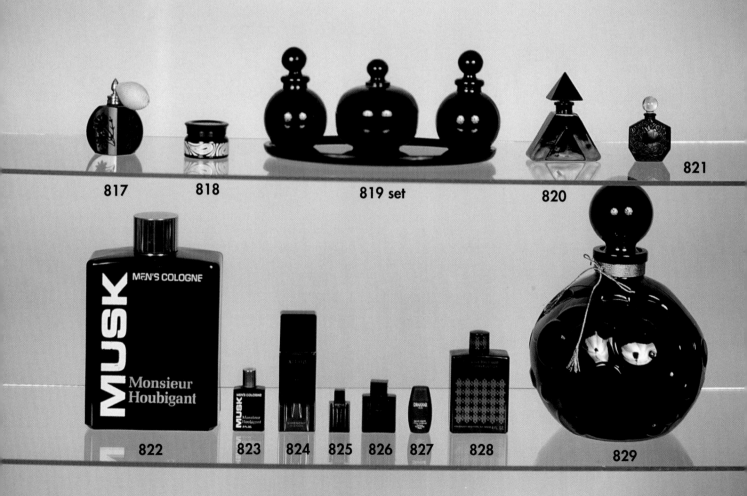

817   818   819 set   820   821

822   823   824   825   826   827   828   829

Perfumes

830   831   832   833   834   835   836

Plates

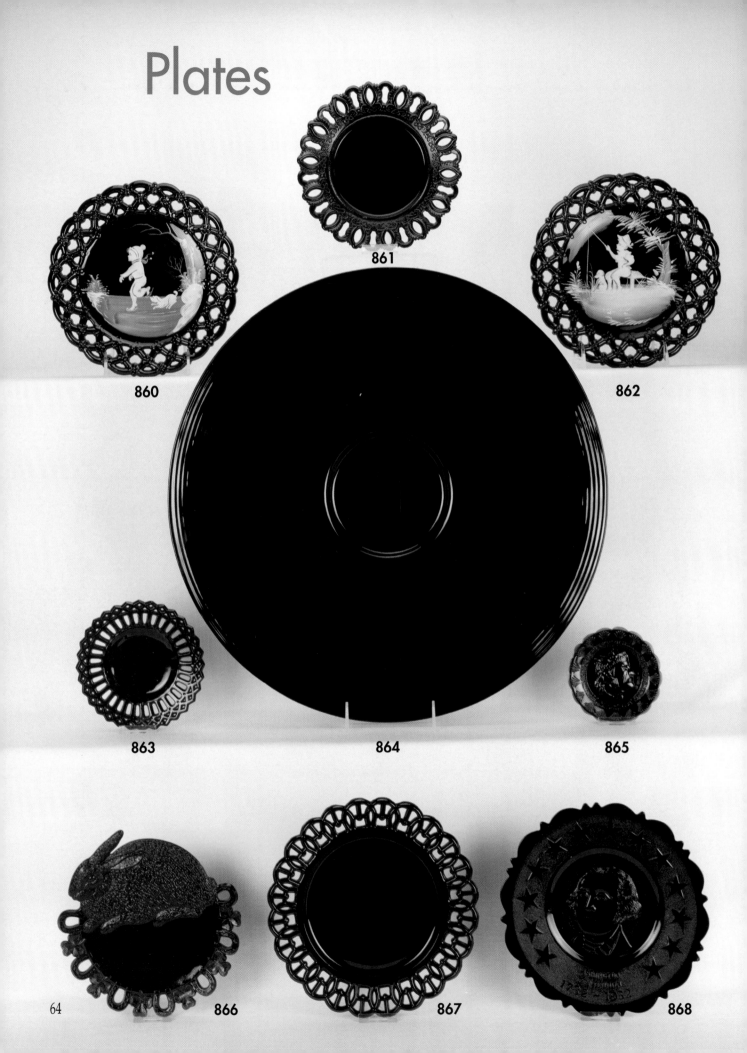

860

861

862

863

864

865

866

867

868

Stands

869   870   871   872

873   874   875   876

878   879   880   881   877

882

883   884   885   886   887

888   889   890   891

892   893   894   895   896

Stemware

897 898 899 900 901 902 903 904

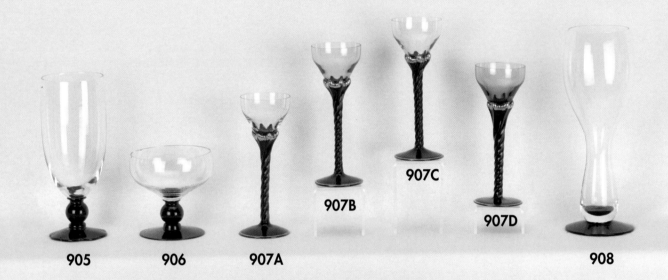

905 906 907A 907B 907C 907D 908

Smoking Items

909 910 911 912 913

Taiwan

914 915 916 917 918 919 920 921

922 923 924 925 926 927 928

929 930 931 932 933 934 935 936

Taiwan

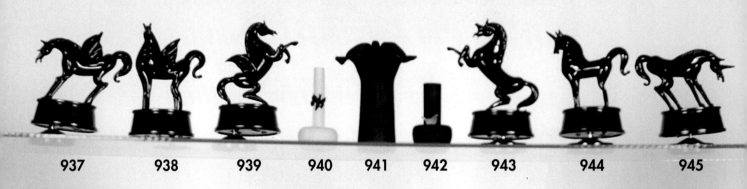

937   938   939   940   941   942   943   944   945

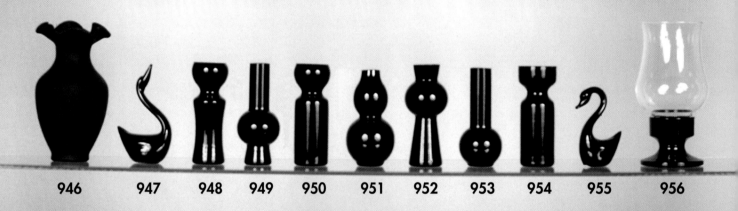

946   947   948   949   950   951   952   953   954   955   956

957   958   959   960   961   962   963   964

Taiwan

965   966   967   968   969   970   971

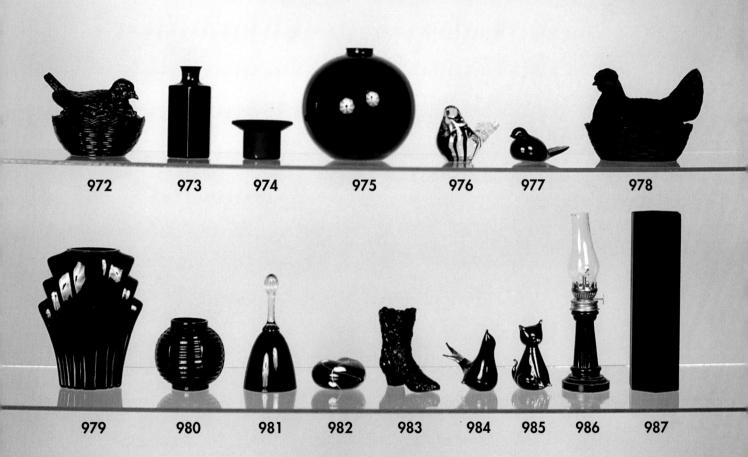

972   973   974   975   976   977   978

979   980   981   982   983   984   985   986   987

Taiwan

988   989   990   991

992   993   994   995   996   997   998   999   1000   1001

1002   1003   1004   1005

1006   1007   1008   1009   1010   1011   1012

Taiwan and Other Imports

1013 1014 1015 1016 1017

1018 1019 1020 1021 1022 1023 1024

1025 1026 1027 1028

Tiara Exclusives

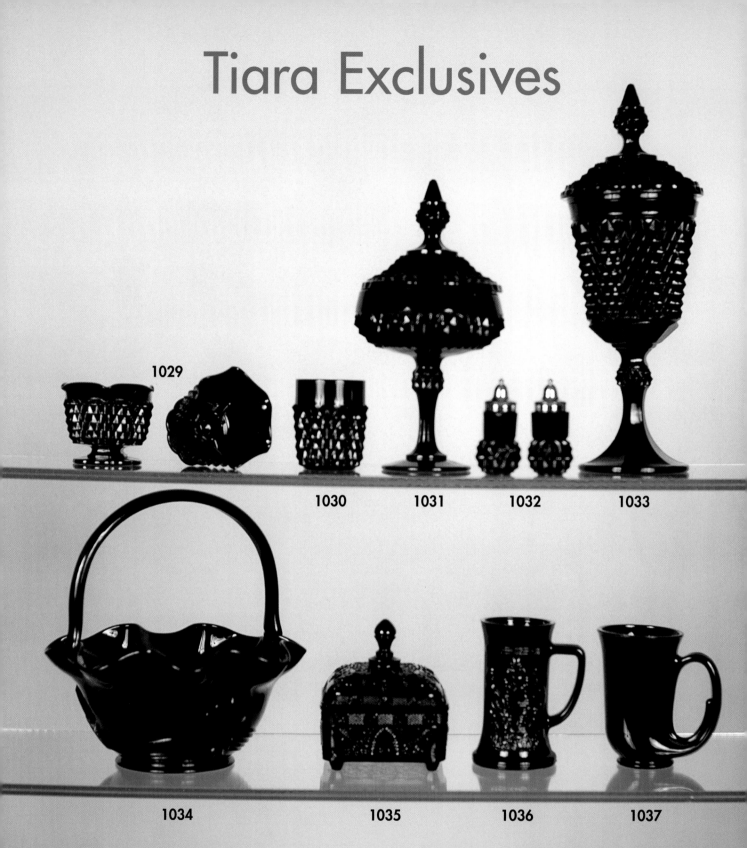

1029

1030   1031   1032   1033

1034   1035   1036   1037

Tiara Exclusives

1038   1039   1040   1041

1042   1043   1044

1045A   1045B   1046   1047   1046

1048   1049   1050   1051   1052

Tiara Exclusives

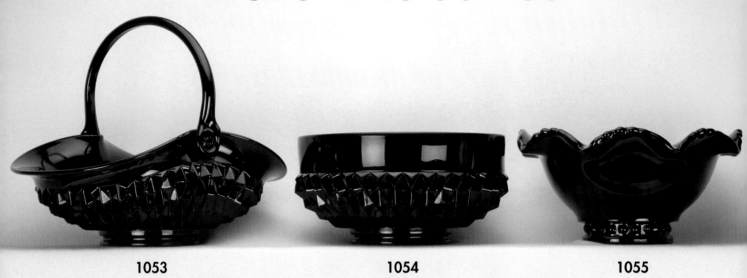

1053   1054   1055

1056   1057   1058   1059

1060   1061   1062

Tiffin

1063   1064   1065   1066   1067

1068   1069   1070   1071

1072   1073   1074   1075

Viking

1076   1077   1078   1079   1080

1081   1082   1083   1084   1085   1086   1085   1084   1087

1088   1089   1090   1091   1092   1093   1094   1095   1096   1097   1098   1097

Dalzell-Viking

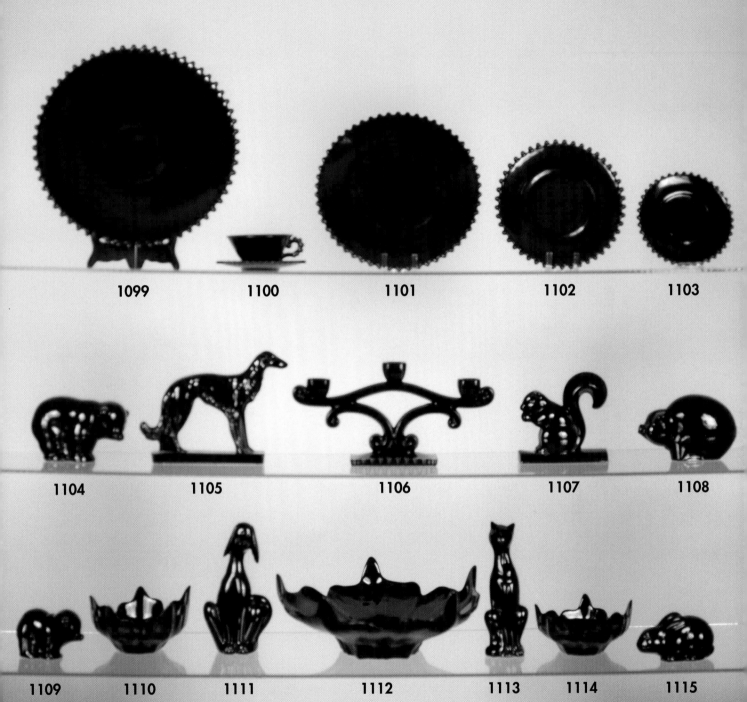

1099   1100   1101   1102   1103

1104   1105   1106   1107   1108

1109   1110   1111   1112   1113   1114   1115

Victorian

1116   1117   1118   1119   1120

1121   1122   1123   1124   1125

1126   1127   1128   1129

1130   1131   1132   1131   1133

Westmoreland

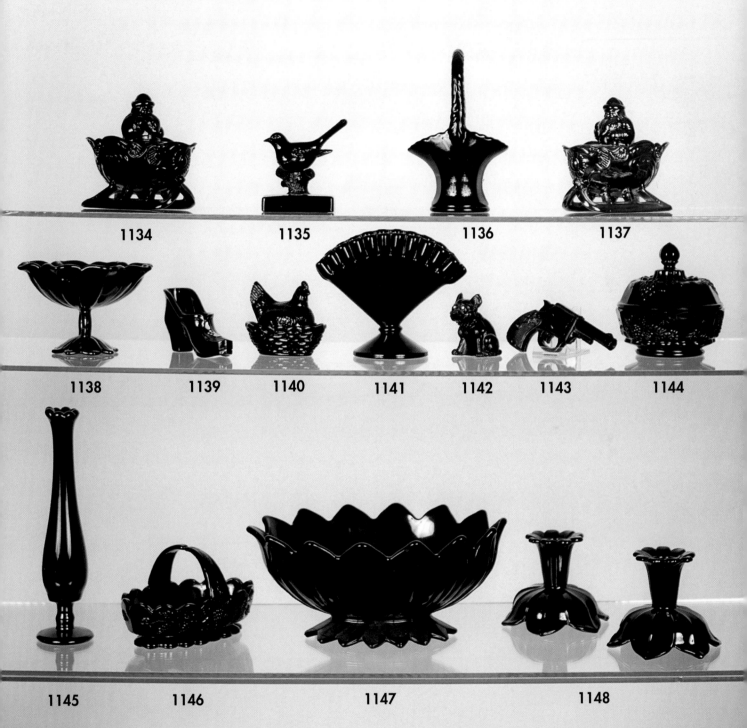

1134   1135   1136   1137

1138   1139   1140   1141   1142   1143   1144

1145   1146   1147   1148

DESIGNED BY
BOB GRAYSON

91-23

91-25

92-09

92-06

91-26

91-27 (tray)

91-24

DESIGNED BY
CHARLES A. BERRY

91-109

91-107

91-108

91-111

91-110

Art Glass selections in ethereal shades, from a 1985
catalog of the Silvestri Corporation, p. 10.

263. Hatpin head (missing the pin), 2" diameter, no markings, circa 1920s.

264. 9" tray, no markings. This could be used for perfume bottles, or for a cream and sugar set.

265. No. 2375 icer liner (missing the crystal insert), Fairfax pattern, 5" wide, 3" high, Fostoria Glass Company 1960s–70s. The pattern was essentially plain (or blank), but some of Fostoria's etchings did appear on Fairfax pieces.

IMPERIAL GLASS COMPANY, P. 30

The Imperial Glass Company of Bellaire, Ohio was a frequent manufacturer of black glass. Imperial's black color first appeared in the early Depression years, and has been made intermittently through the early 1980s. Refer to page 6 for information on the company's trademarks.

266. No. 400/7F bowl, Candlewick pattern with Black Cosmos decoration, 8" diameter, 1937.

267. No. 320 2-handled dish, handpainted Maytime decoration, 6" wide, circa 1930s.

268. No. 400/62D 2-handled plate, Candlewick pattern with handpainted Black Cosmos decoration, 8½" diameter, 1937.

269. No. 320 oval candleholders, handpainted Maytime decoration, 3½" high, circa 1930s.

270. No. 320 oval console bowl, handpainted Maytime decoration, 10½" wide, 5" high, circa 1930s.

271. No. 320 6" footed candy dish, handpainted Maytime decoration, circa 1930s.

272. No. 51855 Club ashtray from 4-piece poker set, 3½" long, marked with IG, 1981.

273. No. 51855 Diamond ashtray from 4-piece bridge set, 4" long, marked with IG, 1981.

274. No. 51855 Spade ashtray from 4-piece bridge set, 3½" long, marked with IG, 1981.

275. No. 51855 Heart ashtray from 4-piece bridge set, 3½" long, marked with IG, 1981.

276. Lace-edged handled tray, 9" diameter, circa 1980s.

277. No. 414 or No. 625 handled sugar, Diamond Quilted pattern, 3¾" high, 1929–32.

278. Footed oval candy dish, 9" long, 3" high, for Tiara Exclusives by the Indiana Glass Company of Dunkirk, Indiana 1970s–80s.

IMPERIAL GLASS COMPANY AND OTHERS, P. 31

279. Horse figurine, 6" high, marked with IG logo, made by Imperial for the Heisey Collectors Association's 1985 Convention. This piece still has the original "bust-off" base.

280. Bull figurine, 7¾" long, 3¾" high, marked with ALIG logo, 1983. Made by Imperial from a Heisey mold, this was a test piece, and only about 30 were reported to have been made in black glass.

281. Tiger figurine, 8" long, 2½" high, marked with ALIG logo, 1982. Also made by Imperial from a Heisey mold, it was reported that only 700 were made in black glass.

282. Pig figurine, 5" long, 3" high, marked with ALIG logo and "Heisey by Imperial" paper label, Heisey mold made by Imperial 1982.

283. Console bowl, 12" diameter, with label, made in Italy 1991.

284. Lawn globe on concrete base, 10" diameter, no markings, circa 1990s. The bottom of this globe has a stem which fits into the concrete base, preventing it from falling.

285. Scottie Dog bookend, 6½" high, marked with IG, Imperial Glass Company 1979. This satin glass Scottie was made in the original Cambridge mold, and sold to the National Cambridge Club as a souvenir piece in 1979. Firing was limited to approximately 400 pieces.

286. Scalloped plate, 14½" diameter, with label, made in Italy 1991.

287. Candle lamp, 10³/₄" high, with label, made by Toscany 1991.

288. Whale figurine, white and black satin glass, 3³/₄" long, with label, made in Taiwan 1989.

289. Snail figurine, crystal and black glass, 4¹/₂" high, with label, Murano Glass circa 1980s.

290. Seagull figurine, white and black satin glass, 5¹/₄" wide, with label, made in Taiwan 1989.

291. 4¹/₂" snail figurine, pink swirls in crystal, Murano Glass circa 1990s.

292. Round vase, 11¹/₂" high, with label, circa 1990s.

293. Top Hat ice bucket, 12" high, 7" wide, with label, made by Stelvia 1987.

294. Cat figurine, 7" long, with label, Murano Glass 1989.

295. 5¹/₂" snail figurine, white and black satin glass, with label, Murano Glass circa 1980s.

296. Dog figurine, 6¹/₂" high, with label, Murano Glass circa 1980s.

297. Cat liquor bottle (held imported wine), 6¹/₂" high, no markings, 1971.

298. Poodle liquor bottle (held imported wine), 6¹/₂" high, no markings, 1971.

299. Bitters bottle, 3" high, marked "Made in Taiwan."

300. Decanter, cased black glass and silver, 12¹/₄" high, with label, Murano Glass circa 1990s.

301. 6 oz. champagne goblet, black crystal, with paper label, 1966.

302. 7 oz. wine goblet, black crystal, with paper label, 1966.

303. 10 oz. water goblet, black crystal, with paper label, 1966.

304. 8 oz. champagne goblet, black satin with flowers, with label, made by Taitu 1987.

305. 4 oz. wine goblet, black satin with flowers, with label, made by Taitu 1987.

306. Flower bud vase, 9¹/₂" high, with label, circa 1980s.

307. Flower pot, handpainted flowers and gold trim, 6¹/₂" high, with label, made by Norleens circa 1980s.

308. Flower bud vase, 9¹/₂" high, with label, circa 1980s.

309. 6 oz. wine glass, with label, circa 1990s.

310. 6 oz. wine glass, crystal glass on black stem, with label, circa 1990s. This advertising glass was sold as part of a gift set containing two glasses and a bottle of Freixenet liquor.

311. Owl figurine, cased black glass and silver, 7¹/₂" high, with label, Murano Glass circa 1980s.

312. Candleholders, 8" high, with label, made by Toscany circa 1980s.

313. Console bowl with handpainted flowers, 8¹/₄" diameter, 4¹/₄" high, with label, circa 1980s.

314. 4¹/₂" rose bowl, with label, circa 1990s.

315. Designer vase, cased black and milk glass, 6¹/₂" high, with label, circa 1990s.

316. Swirled bowl, black and milk glass, 10³/₄" diameter, no markings but probably made by Murano Glass circa 1990s.

317. Stemmed 8 oz. wine, milk glass lining, no markings.

318. Stemmed 2 oz. cordial, milk glass lining, no markings.

319. Venetian flower vase, applied gold decoration with porcelain flowers, 6¹/₄" high, with label, circa 1990s. Black is a color that is rarely seen in Venetian glass.

320. Large plate, Greek Key design, 12¹/₂" diameter, with label, made by Cive circa 1990s.

321. Large bowl, Greek Key design, 14" diameter, with label, made by Cive circa 1990s.

322. Clown figurine, multicolored free form, 10" high, with label, Murano Glass circa 1960s.

323. Clown figurine, multicolored free form, 9" high, with label, Murano Glass circa 1960s.

324. Cordial set with 1 oz. glasses, 4" decanter and 7" tray, no markings.

325. Vase, multicolored over black, $9^3/_4$" high, no markings but probably made by Murano Glass.

JEWELRY, P. 35

All the jewelry on this page dates pre-1940s. Manufacturers and dates of manufacture are not known.

326. Single-strand beaded necklace with square, faceted, oblong and round beads, 45" long.

327. Marquis pin, 2" diameter.

328. Sweater pin, 7" long.

329A-T. Buttons ranging in size from $^1/_4$" to $1^1/_4$".

330. Cameo ring, $1^3/_4$" wide.

331. Oval ring, 1" long.

332. Faceted heart pendant, 2" long.

333. Faceted earrings, clip-on, 1" diameter.

334. Faceted earrings, clip-on, 1" diameter.

335. Earrings set in metal frame, 1" diameter.

336. Marquis and rhinestone pin, $1^1/_4$" diameter.

337. 16" necklace with black and crystal beads.

338. Teardrop earrings with screw backs, 1" long.

339. Faceted single-strand necklace, 54" long.

340. Flapper's beads, 73" long.

341. Solid bracelet with multicolored design.

342. High-heel shoe clips, $2^1/_2$" long.

343. Beaded scarf pin, $2^1/_2$" long.

344. Solid bracelet.

345. 3" belt buckle.

346. Beaded shoe buckles, celluloid beads.

JEWELRY, PP. 36

Manufacturer and dates of manufacture are not documented for the jewelry on this page.

347. Triple-strand faceted necklace, 14" long.

348. Single-strand faceted necklace, 16" long.

349. Single-strand necklace, beads of multiple sizes, 16" long.

350. Single-strand faceted necklace, large beads, 16" long.

351. Double-strand beaded necklace, black carnival, 20" long.

352. Single-strand necklace, diamond-shaped beads, 18" long.

353. Multi-beaded earrings, clip-on, $1^1/_4$" dia.

354. Earrings with marquis stones, clip-on, $1^1/_4$" diameter.

355. Oval faceted earrings, clip-on, $1^1/_4$" dia.

356. Beaded earrings, black carnival, clip-on, 1" diameter.

357. Round faceted earrings, clip-on, $1^1/_4$" dia.

358. Marquis earrings, clip-on, $1^1/_4$" diameter.

359. Inverted cameo pin, 2" long.

360. Bead and rhinestone earrings, clip-on, 2" long.

361. Clip-on bracelet with multi-shaped stones, 2" wide.

362. Cameo pin, white cameo on black glass $1^3/_4$" long.

363. Necklace with bead and rhinestone pendant, 1$^1/_2$" wide.

364. Cameo pendant or pin, gold cameo on black glass, 2" long.

365. Cut-glass pin, 1$^1/_2$" long.

366. Flower pin with marquis stones, 2$^1/_4$" wide.

367. Choker, 14" long.

368. Chain with black teardrop in silver pendant, 15$^1/_2$" long.

369. Faceted button earrings, clip-on, 1$^1/_2$" wide.

370. Faceted beaded bracelet, 7" long.

371. Brooch with pearls, 2" long.

372. Pin with marquisites, 2$^1/_2$" long.

373. Beaded choker, 13" long.

374. Cameo pin with black cameo on black glass, 2" long.

375. Choker with marquis stones, 13" long.

376. Faceted button, 1$^1/_4$" diameter.

377. Faceted button, 1" diameter.

378. Necklace with black and white glass beads, 18" long.

379. Faceted button, 1" diameter.

380. Faceted button, 1$^1/_2$" diameter.

KITCHENWARE, P. 37

This page features a very nice, but inexpensive set of dishes and accessories that have been imported from France over the past ten years. Most pieces are still available at retail outlets.

381. Octagonal platter, 13" wide, made by Arcoroc circa 1990s.

382. Octagonal dinner plate, 10$^1/_2$" wide, made by Arcoroc circa 1990s.

383. Octagonal salad or dessert plate, 7$^1/_2$" wide, made by Arcoroc circa 1990s.

384. Candleholders, 1$^3/_4$" wide, made by Luminarc circa 1990s.

385. Salad bowl, 9" wide, 4" high, made by Luminarc circa 1990s.

386. 5" canister, made by Luminarc circa 1990s.

387. Salt and pepper shakers, 3$^1/_2$" high, made by Luminarc circa 1990s.

388. 7" canister, made by Luminarc circa 1990s.

389. 9" canister, made by Luminarc circa 1990s.

390. Cereal bowl, 5$^3/_4$" wide, made by Arcoroc circa 1990s.

391. 8 oz. mug, made by Arcoroc circa 1990s.

392. 4$^1/_2$" covered sugar and matching 3" creamer, made by Arcoroc circa 1990s.

393. 4 oz. wine glass, crystal on black stem, made by Luminarc circa 1990s.

394. Octagonal clock, battery-operated, made by Luminarc circa 1990s.

395. 8 oz. water glass, crystal on black stem, made by Luminarc circa 1990s.

KITCHENWARE, PP. 38–40

396. Sugar bowl (shown without matching lid), 3" wide, Oneida Crystal circa 1990s.

397. Demitasse plate, 5" wide, made by Arcoroc, France circa 1990s.

398. 6 oz. demitasse cup, made by Arcoroc, France circa 1990s.

399. Demitasse plate, 4$^1/_2$" wide, made by Arcoroc, France circa 1990s.

400. 2 oz. demitasse cup, made by Arcoroc, France circa 1990s.

401. 3" relish bowl, unknown maker circa 1990s.

402. Oblong serving dish, 11$^1/_4$" long, unknown maker circa 1990s.

403. Mixing bowl, 8" diameter, unknown maker circa 1990s.

404. Oblong serving bowl, 7" long, unknown maker circa 1990s.

405. 1½-quart open casserole, Corningware, Corning Incorporated circa 1990s.

406. 2½-quart oval casserole with cover, Corningware, Corning Incorporated circa 1990s.

407. 1½-quart round casserole, Corningware, Corning Incorporated circa 1990s.

408. 8 oz. wine glass, Fostoria Glass Co. 1978.

409. 10 oz. tumbler, unknown maker circa 1980s.

410. 4 oz. wine glass, promotional piece that came in a gift set with a bottle of wine, unknown maker circa 1990s.

411. 6 oz. water glass, black satin with raised rose design, unknown maker.

412. Toothpick holder, marked "In memory of Elvis Presley August 16, 1977" in silver, Rosso's Wholesale Glass.

413. 5 oz. wine glass, crystal on black stem, unknown maker circa 1990s.

414. 7 oz. water glass, crystal on black stem, unknown maker circa 1990s.
415. Storage jar, 5" high, imported circa 1990s.

416. 5" storage jar, made in Italy circa 1990s.

417. 4" storage jar, made in Italy circa 1990s.

418. 6" storage jar, made in Italy circa 1990s.

419. Cameo ice bucket, 6" high, with label, for Tiara Exclusives by the Indiana Glass Company of Dunkirk, Indiana circa 1980s.

420. Reamer or juicer, 5" diameter, for Edna Barnes by Mosser Glass Company 1981.

421. Cereal bowl, 5" diameter, with label, for Tiara Exclusives by the Indiana Glass Company of Dunkirk, Indiana circa 1980s.

422. Salad bowl, 10" diameter, with label, for Tiara Exclusives by the Indiana Glass Company of Dunkirk, Indiana circa 1980s.

423. 12 oz. tumbler, unknown maker.

424. Cruet with crystal stopper, unknown maker.

425. Cloverleaf plate, 8" diameter, Hazel-Atlas Glass Company 1930–36.

426. 6 oz. syrup pitcher, unknown maker circa 1920s–30s.

427. Matching 8" underplate, unknown maker circa 1920s–30s.

428. Tumble-up decanter (came with a glass that covers the top), 6½" high, unknown maker.

429. Violet bowl (held a flower frog), 3¾" high, New Martinsville Glass Company.

430. Handled sugar bowl, 4" high, unknown maker circa 1920s–30s.

431. Salad set with wooden tray, wooden salt and pepper shakers, black glass relish bowl and oil cruet, unknown maker.

432. 8 oz. cup, unknown maker.

433. 8 oz. pepper shaker, McKee Glass Company circa 1930s.

434. Pedestal sugar bowl or candy dish with handpainted decoration, 4" high, unknown maker circa 1930s.

435. Crystal cruet set with black stoppers, 6" wide, 4" high, unknown maker.

436. 5 oz. creamer, unknown maker.

437. 5 oz. creamer, unknown maker.

438. 2½" geometric open salt, unknown maker.

439. 5 oz. footed creamer, unknown maker.

440. 3 oz. creamer, black satin, unknown maker.

441. 2 oz. souvenir shot glass with "Wyoming," unknown maker circa 1990s.

442. 2 oz. souvenir shot glass with "Boston," made in Taiwan circa 1990s.

443. Salt and pepper shakers, black satin, 4^1/$_4$" high, unknown maker circa 1990s.

444. Salt shaker, 5" high, unknown maker circa 1930s.

445. Footed salt and pepper shakers, ribbed horizontally, 3^1/$_2$" high, marked "HA" for Hazel-Atlas Glass Company circa 1930s.

446. No. 1639 footed sherbet, ebony bowl on jade foot and stem, 3^1/$_4$" high, Fenton Art Glass Company circa 1930.

447. Salt and pepper shakers, crystal on black base, 3^3/$_4$" high, unknown maker circa 1930s.

448. 2 oz. advertising shot glass, "Ocean Pacific Spring 1991," unknown maker circa 1991.

449. 2 oz. shot glass with Crown Royal crest, Colorado Rockies logo, marked "L" for Libbey Glass Company of Dallas, TX 1991.

450. 2 oz. advertising shot glass, marked "Imported Rumple Minze," made in Korea circa 1990s.

451. 6 oz. drinking glass, unknown maker.

452. 1^3/$_4$" napkin ring with painted decoration, with label, made in India circa 1980s.

453. Handled cream and sugar tray, 6" wide, unknown maker circa 1920s–30s.

454. Salt or pepper shaker, ribbed horizontally, 3^1/$_2$" high, marked "HA" for Hazel-Atlas Glass Company circa 1930s.

455. Dresser tray, 6^1/$_2$" long, unknown maker.

456. Hollow, faceted knife rest, 6" long, unknown maker.

LAMPS, P. 41

457. Dresser lamp, blue milk glass on black glass base, 8^3/$_4$" high (from base to top of fixture), unknown maker.

458. Table lamp, gold trim, 10^1/$_2$" high, unknown maker circa 1930s.

459. Table lamp brass fixtures and shade are not original, 27" high, unknown maker circa 1930s.

460. Scottie Dog lamp, 6" high from base to top of fixture, unknown maker.

461. Dresser lamp with original shade, 10^1/$_4$" high from base to top of fixture.

L. E. SMITH AND OTHERS, PP. 42–43

The L. E. Smith Glass Company was established in 1911 in Mt. Pleasant, Pennsylvania at the old Anchor Glass plant. Originally a manufacturer of containers and jars, the plant eventually put out tableware and decorative items, producing black glass from the mid-1920s until about 1935. Some black glass was made again in the 1950s. After acquiring the Greensburg Glass Works in 1920, L. E. Smith also manufactured some black glass at the Greensburg factory.

462. Hurricane lamp, 12" high, L. E. Smith Glass Company 1992.

463. Star paperweight, 5" high, L. E. Smith Glass Company 1992.

464. 5" oval paperweight, L. E. Smith Glass Company 1992.

465. Hurricane lamp, 9" high, L. E. Smith Glass Company 1992.

466. 7" Duck covered dish, L. E. Smith Glass Company 1992.

467. Hexagon paperweight, 3" high, L. E. Smith Glass Company 1992.

468. Piano box, 6^1/$_2$" wide, L. E. Smith Glass Company 1992.

469. Airplane kaleidoscope with trade marbles in the propeller that change colors, 7" long, 9" wide (across wings), signed and numbered, made by The Glass Anvil 1990.

470. Biplane kaleidoscope, 13" wide (across wings), 9" long, signed and numbered, made by The Glass Anvil 1990.

471. Candle lamp, frosted shade on black glass base, 7¹/₂" high, L. E. Smith Glass Company 1992.

472. Decorated vase, 9" high, unknown maker circa 1930s.

473. Decorated vase, 8¹/₂" high, unknown maker circa 1930s.

474. Handled sandwich tray, 10" diameter, L. E. Smith Glass Company circa 1930s.

475. Flared vase, 6" high, unknown maker circa 1920s–30s.

476. No. 1938 1 quart casserole with decorated lid, 7" diameter, marked "Fry Ovenglass 1938," H. C. Fry Glass Company of Rochester, Pennsylvania circa 1920s. Most Fry Oven-glass was marked with mold number, size and, in some cases, patent date. On this particular piece, 1938 refers to the mold number.

477. Handpainted candlesticks with gold and floral decoration, 9" high, Diamond Glassware Co. of Indiana, Pennsylvania 1925–32.

478. Handpainted console bowl with gold and floral decoration, 10" diameter, Diamond Glassware Co. of Indiana, Pa. 1925–32.

479. Handled beverage tray, originally came with crystal cordials, 6" diameter, L. E. Smith Glass Company circa 1930s.

480. No. 1022/4 three-footed console bowl, 9" wide, L. E. Smith Glass Company circa 1930s.

481. No. 1022/4 three-footed console bowl, 6" wide, L. E. Smith Glass Company circa 1930s.

L. E. Smith and McKee, p. 44

482. Tom & Jerry punch bowl with silver writing, 11¹/₂" diameter, marked mckee in circle, McKee Glass Company circa 1950s.

483. Tom & Jerry 8 oz. punch cups, marked mckee in circle, McKee Glass Company circa 1950s.

484. Bulb bowl, 7" wide, 5¹/₂" high, McKee Glass Company 1931.

485. Console bowl, Autumn pattern, 12" wide, 5¹/₂" high, McKee Glass Company 1934.

486. Handled sandwich tray, Mt. Pleasant pattern, 10" diameter, L. E. Smith Glass Co. circa 1930s.

487. Platter, Mt. Pleasant pattern, 13¹/₂" diameter, L. E. Smith Glass Company circa 1930s.

488. No. 505 Handled nut dish, Mt. Pleasant pattern, 8¹/₄" diameter, L. E. Smith Glass Co.y circa 1930s.

489. Flower pot and saucer, 4" high, L. E. Smith Glass Company circa 1930s.

490. 5¹/₂" flower pot and saucer, L. E. Smith Glass Company circa 1930s.

491. Lamb figurine, 2¹/₄" long, marked with C in a circle, L. E. Smith Glass Company circa 1930s.

492. Wigwam candlestick, 3¹/₄" high, L. E. Smith Glass Company 1935.

493. 5-piece table set, Mt. Pleasant pattern, consisting of open creamer, open sugar, salt and pepper shakers, and tray, L. E. Smith Glass Company circa 1930s.

Luncheon Sets, pp. 45–46

494. 8¹/₄" plate, Mayfair pattern, Fostoria Glass Company circa 1930s.

495A–B. 5" saucer with cup, Mayfair pattern, Fostoria Glass Company circa 1930s.

496A–B. Embellished Ebon crystal cup with 5¹/₂" square saucer, Morgantown Glass Works of Morgantown, W Va. 1931.

497. Embellished Ebon square plate, 7¹/₂" wide, Morgantown Glass Works of Morgantown, West Virginia 1931.

498. Embellished Ebon square platter, 9¹/₂" wide with handles, Morgantown Glass Works of Morgantown, West Virginia 1931.

499. 8" octagonal plate, Morgantown Glass Works of Morgantown, West Virginia 1931.

500A–B. 5" octagonal saucer with cup, Morgantown Glass Works of Morgantown, West Virginia 1931.

501A–B. Hexagonal cup with 5" saucer, unknown maker circa 1930s.

502. 7" hexagonal plate, unknown maker circa 1930s.

503. Octagonal plate with floral pattern on back, 7¹⁄₂" wide, unknown maker circa 1930s.

504A–B. Octagonal 5" saucer with cup, floral pattern on the back, unknown maker circa 1930s.

505A–B. Cup with 6" saucer, Mt. Pleasant pattern, L. E. Smith Glass Company circa 1930s.

506. 8" plate, Mt. Pleasant pattern, L. E. Smith Glass Company circa 1930s.

507. 7³⁄₄" round plate, unknown maker circa 1930s.

508A–B. 5³⁄₄" saucer with cup, unknown maker circa 1930s.

509. Cup, Cambridge Glass Company circa 1929.

510. Line No. 99 saucer, 5³⁄₄" wide, Diamond Glassware Company of Indiana, Pa. 1930.

511. Line No. 99 plate, 8" wide, Diamond Glassware Company of Indiana, Pa. 1930.

512. Line No. 34 plate, 7¹⁄₂" diameter, New Martinsville Glass Company circa 1930s.

513A–B. Line No. 34 5¹⁄₂" saucer with cup, New Martinsville Glass Company circa 1930s.

514A–B. Cup with 6" saucer, Do Si Do pattern, L. E. Smith Glass Company circa 1930s.

515. 8" plate, Do Si Do pattern, L. E. Smith Glass Company circa 1930s.

516. 8" plate, unknown maker circa 1930s.

517A–B. Plain cup with 5¹⁄₂" saucer, Hazel-Atlas Glass Company circa 1930s. While this set is plain, the same set is also made with the Clover Leaf and Sterling decorations.

518. Plain plate, 7¹⁄₂" diameter, Hazel-Atlas Glass Company circa 1930s. This plate is also made with the Clover Leaf and Sterling decorations.

MINIATURES, P. 47

To fully appreciate how small these items are, refer to the quarter shown in the lower portion of this photograph. Figures 519–45 are hand blown.

519. Dog, unknown maker circa 1930s.

520. Horse, made in China circa 1980s.

521. Family of cats, made in U. S. A. 1990.

522. Marble people, made in U. S. A. 1993.

523. Dog, made in U. S. A. circa 1930s.

524. Dog, made in U. S. A. circa 1960s.

525A–F. Vases, made in U. S. A. circa 1980s.

526. Swan with stretched neck, made in U. S. A. circa 1950s.

527. Skunk, unknown maker circa 1950s.

528. Seal, made in U. S. A. circa 1990s.

529. Penguin, made in U. S. A. circa 1970s.

530. Cat, black satin, made in U. S. A. circa 1920s–30s.

531. Three Mice, made in U. S. A. circa 1970s.

532. Mouse, made in U. S. A. circa 1920s–30s.

533. Cat, made in U. S. A. circa 1920s–30s.

534. Dog, made in U. S. A. circa 1930s.

535. Seal, made in U. S. A. circa 1970s.

536. Goose, made in U. S. A. circa 1970s.

537. Marble cow, made in U. S. A. circa 1990s.

538. Hummingbird, made in U. S. A. circa 1990s.

539. Leaping horse, made in China circa 1980s.

540. "Coke" marble, made in U. S. A. circa 1980s.

541. "Batman" marble, made in U. S. A. circa 1980s.

542. Galloping horse, made in China circa 1980s.

543. Horse, made in China circa 1980s.

544. Bucking horse, made in China circa 1980s.

545. Horse, made in China circa 1980s.

MISCELLANY, PP. 48–58

546. 8¹/₂" bowl, Stork and Rushes pattern with beaded band, black carnival, made for L. G. Wright Glass Company 1995.

547. 4" candlesticks, unknown maker circa 1990s.

548. 7¹/₂" tobacco jar, Grape and Cable with Thumbprint pattern (made from Fenton mold), Rosso's Wholesale Glass 1968–69.

549. 8¹/₂" bowl, Monarch pattern, with label, for Tiara Exclusives by the Indiana Glass Company of Dunkirk, Indiana circa 1980s.

550. English Hobnail basket, 9" high, has keystone WG mark, made from Westmoreland mold, L. G. Wright Glass Co. circa 1990s.

551. Kitchen wall clock, 12" diameter, with label, for Tiara Exclusives by the Indiana Glass Company of Dunkirk, Indiana circa 1980s.

552. Hatpin, unknown maker circa 1930s.

553. Hatpin holder, 7" high, imported circa 1980s.

554. Hatpin, unknown maker circa 1930s.

555. Insulator with milk and black slag glass, 3³/₄" high, marked "1993" for the National Insulators Association (NIA) Convention in Denver, Colorado, unknown maker.

556. 10 oz. souvenir mug, has pewter logo for Elitch Gardens of Denver, Colorado, Libbey Glass Company 1997.

557. Air freshener, black satin, 5¹/₄" high, made in U. S. A. by Bon Air.

558. 10 oz. mug with Eagle engraving, marked "L" for Libbey Glass Company 1997. These mugs are purchased by local artists and engraved on request.

559. 12¹/₂" oval console bowl, unknown maker.

560. Candle lamp, satin glass shade on black base, 8¹/₂" high, imported 1997.

561. Ink bottle with slanted side, 4" wide, 3¹/₂" high, unmarked. The slanted side allows the bottle to rest at a tilt without spilling ink.

562. Flower pot, 3¹/₂" high, L. E. Smith Glass Company circa 1930s.

563. Roller pad and tray (used to moisten labels and envelopes), 4" long, marked "Zephyr American Corp. NYC," Rolodex Corp.

564. Sugar shaker (this probably had a chrome lid), 3" high, unknown maker circa 1930s.

565. 6" Lemon sculpture, handblown, unknown maker.

566. 2-piece Watermark Detector (for use with stamps), 3" wide, 2¹/₂" high, unknown maker.

567. Tomato sculpture, handblown, 3¹/₂" wide, unknown maker.

568. Razor blade sharpener, 3" long, unknown maker.

569. Furniture coaster, 2" diameter, marked "HA" for Hazel-Atlas Glass Company circa 1930s.

570. Curtain tieback, 3¹/₂" wide, unknown maker circa 1920s–30s.

571. 2¹/₂" doorknob, unknown maker 1920s–30s.

572. 2¹/₄" doorknob, unknown maker 1920s–30s.

573. 3¹/₂" birdfeeder, unknown maker 1920s–30s.

574. Drawer knob, 1¼" wide, unknown maker circa 1920s.

575. Drawer pull, 4¼" wide, unknown maker circa 1920s.

576. 2½" stopper, unknown maker 1920s–30s.

577. 1⅛" stopper, unknown maker 1920s–30s.

578. 2" stopper, unknown maker circa 1920s–30s.

579. Flower stopper, 2½" high, Fenton Art Glass Company circa 1920s–30s.

580. 2" stopper, unknown maker circa 1920s–30s.

581. 1¼" stopper, unknown maker 1920s–30s.

582. 1½" stopper, unknown maker 1920s–30s.

583. 3" stopper, unknown maker circa 1920s–30s.

584. Light fixture, unknown maker circa 1930s.

585. 3" black glass lens, unknown maker.

586. Jewel accessory (with three tiny holes for attaching to clothing or shoes), 2" diameter, unknown maker circa 1920s–30s.

587. Worry stone whimsey, 2" long, Fostoria Glass Company circa 1980s.

588. Handblown twisted cane, 32½" long, made in U. S. A. circa 1980s.

589. "Artie Penguin" figurine, 3" high, Boyd's Crystal Art Glass 1984–88.

590. "Willy Mouse" figurine, 2" high, Boyd's Crystal Art Glass 1991.

591. 14" platter, with label, made in Italy 1990.

592. Choker and earring set, unknown maker circa 1875–1900. This jewelry set belonged to Baby Doe Tabor of the Tabor family. The Tabors were renowned for their role in settling Central City, Colorado (known as the "Richest Square Mile on Earth" during the Gold Rush era).

593. Hurricane lamp, 8" high (to fixture), Dalzell,

Gilmore & Leighton Company of Findlay, Ohio 1897.

594. Mary Gregory plate, 8" diameter, marked with keystone WG, Westmoreland Glass Company circa 1950s.

595. Handblown fish, 5" long, unknown maker circa 1990s.

596. 8¾" bowl with nutcracker, unknown maker circa 1920s–30s.

597. 10" vase, unknown maker circa 1920s–30s.

598. Decanter tray (came with a crystal decanter and six cordial glasses), 8¼" long, unknown maker circa 1920s–30s.

599. Salon nail tray, marked "Theon," unknown maker.

600. Souvenir vase, 7¾" high, marked "Rex, New Orleans 1917" in silver, unknown maker.

601. No. 725 twisted candlesticks, 10" high, Harry Northwood Company circa 1920s.

602. Enameled basin, 14" diameter, made in Italy circa early 1900s.

603. Covered box with gold decoration, 5" long, unknown maker circa 1920s–30s.

604. Monogrammed cigarette box, 4½" wide, unknown maker circa 1930s.

605. No. 137 covered candy box with clown's head for finial, Beaumont Company circa 1920s.

606. Cigarette box and cover, 7" long, New Martinsville Glass Company circa 1930s.

607. Basket with crystal handle, 9½" wide, unknown maker.

608. Decanter, 12" high, unknown maker.

609. 8" flower bowl, unknown maker.

610. 9" decanter, cased crystal over black with orange glass on interior, cut on the front is a

portrait of Elton John, unknown maker.

611. Large 11" vase, wide at top, unknown maker. This piece is extremely heavy and has a hole drilled through the bottom, possibly to be used as a lamp.

612. Three-light candlestick, 9" long, unknown maker circa 1920s–30s.

613. 9" shallow bowl, unknown maker circa 1920s.

614. Flower box with Lion decoration, 9" long, 5" high, McKee Glass Company circa 1930s.

615. Footed individual salt, 2^1/$_2$" wide, made in England, British Glass Company circa 1860s–90s.

616. Footed sugar, 5" wide, 3^3/$_4$" high, made in England, British Glass Company circa 1860s–90s.

617. 6^3/$_4$" footed compote, unknown maker.

618. Daffodil vase, 4^3/$_4$" high, unknown maker circa 1930s.

619. Slender bud vase with decoration, 10" high, unknown maker circa 1930s.

620. Wide vase, 9" high, unknown maker circa 1990s.

621. Bud vase with decoration, 10" high, with label, Maryland Glass Company 1929–33.

622. 6" vase, unknown maker.

623. Line No. 33 Modernistic vase, 3-sided, 8^1/$_2$" high, New Martinsville Glass Company circa 1930s.

624. Fluted vase, 6^1/$_4$" high, unknown maker circa 1930s.

625. 6^1/$_2$" vase, orange mixed with black glass, marked "Czechoslovakia."

626. Triangular vase, 9^3/$_4$" high, unknown maker.

627. 3-footed candy dish, 4^1/$_2$" high, marked "Czechoslovakia."

628. 7" vase, Mikasa of Japan 1981.

629. Lonely Blackbird figurine, 3" high, signed Titan Art Glass 1996.

630. Grandad Swan figurine, 4" high, signed Titan Art Glass 1996.

631. Baby Blackbird figurine, 2" high, signed Titan Art Glass 1996.

632. No. 3872 candle bowl, 6^1/$_2$" diameter, Fenton Art Glass Company 1968–74.

633. Adult Swan figurine, 3^1/$_4$" high, signed Titan Art Glass 1996.

634. 6^3/$_4$" fluted bud vase, unknown maker.

635. Lonely Blackbird votive holder, 4^1/$_2$" high, signed Titan Art Glass 1996.

636. Mini Blackbird, 1^1/$_4$" high, signed Titan Art Glass 1996.

637. Baby Swan figurine, 2^1/$_2$" high, signed Titan Art Glass 1996.

638. Swan soap dish, 5^1/$_4$" side, signed Titan Art Glass 1996.

639. 8" vase, cased crystal over black with gold swirls, milk glass lining, made in Italy.

640. 9^1/$_2$" decanter, stopper and decoration are made of pewter, unknown maker circa 1930s.

641A. Line No. 700 8 oz. goblet, opaque black, Westmoreland Glass Company circa 1930s.

641B. Line No. 700 8 oz. goblet, black satin, Westmoreland Glass Company circa 1930s.

642. Bud vase, 9^1/$_2$" high, with label, Fenton Art Glass Company circa 1980s.

643. Bud vase, 11^1/$_2$" high, with label, Fenton Art Glass Company circa 1980s.

644. 8 oz. tumbler, made in France, by Val St. Lambert circa 1950s–60s.

645. 20 oz. spill cup, made in France, by Val St. Lambert circa 1950s–60s.

646. 4" Penguin planter, unknown maker.

647. 10½" vase with silver decoration, signed Czechoslovakia.

648. 6" vase, unknown maker circa 1920s–30s.

649. Victorian vase, 8" high, unknown maker circa early 1900s.

650. 2-piece epergne, 6" high, possibly German, unknown maker circa early 1900s.

651. No. 643 covered jelly or bon bon, 5¾" diameter, H. Northwood Company circa 1920s.

652. Shallow candy dish, 6" diameter, unknown maker circa 1920s–30s.

653. 6" saucer, unknown maker.

654. No. 1211 3" candlesticks, black satin with painted flowers and gilt edges, Westmoreland Glass Company circa 1930s.

655. 11" vase, Westmoreland Glass circa 1980s.

656. Line No. 416 Cornucopia bowl, 12" wide, New Martinsville Glass Company 1941.

657. Creamer, sugar and tray, Dalzell-Viking Glass Company 1989.

658. 4½" footed candy box with cover, unknown maker.

659. Line No. 1067 "Three Ball" candlesticks, 3" high, Westmoreland Glass Company circa 1950s.

660. Flower basket, black satin, 13¾" high, Tiffin Glass (U. S. Glass Factory R) 1929–41.

661A–B. Creamer and sugar, Egg Harbor line, Liberty Glass Works of Egg Harbor, New Jersey 1929.

662. "Crow's Foot" divided candy dish, 7" wide, Paden City Glass Mfg. Company circa 1930s.

663. 12" bowl, Doric pattern, Westmoreland Glass Company circa 1980s.

664. No. 8098 footed rose bowl (one-piece), 7¼" wide, 5" high, Tiffin Glass (U. S. Glass Factory R) 1924–34.

665. 6" Starfish, Pairpoint Glass Works 1998. When I visited the factory, I learned that Pairpoint never makes black glass as a sales item. When the color they are working on turns out wrong, they add chemicals to the formula to make it black. Very few Pairpoint items in black glass will ever be found or identified.

666. 7½" flower bowl on stand, decorated black satin, Tiffin Glass (U. S. Glass Factory R) 1924–34.

667. 10¼" candlestick, signed Czechoslovakia.

668. No. 117 Garret candlestick, black satin, 8½" high, Paden City Glass Mfg. Company circa 1930s.

669. 10" sandwich tray, etched "Lela Bird" decoration, Paden City Glass Mfg. Company 1929.

670. No. 117 Garret candlestick, opaque black, 8½" high, Paden City Glass Mfg. Company circa 1930s.

671. 7" candlestick, black crackle glass, unknown maker circa 1920s–30s.

672. Divided candy dish in chrome basket, 8½" long, unknown maker circa 1920s–30s.

673. Oil lamp, 8" high to top of hurricane, marked "Japan."

674. Open-handled bowl, 8" diameter, unknown maker.

675. Oil lamp, 8" high to top of hurricane, marked "Romance Light," made in Japan.

676. No. 628 3½" candlestick, Cambridge Glass Company circa 1930s.

677. 7½" basket with crystal handle, unknown maker.

678. Playing card tray, unknown maker circa 1930s.

679. Square candleholder, 2" high, unknown maker circa 1920s–30s.

680. Photo plate, 5" diameter, sold at fairs and personalized by adding a photo (this one features the cover of my first book), made in Korea 1995.

681. Witch's ball, 3$^1/_2$" diameter, unknown maker circa 1930s.

682. Spittoon, 2$^3/_4$" high, 2" wide, unknown maker circa 1920s–30s.

683. Salt and pepper shakers, 1$^1/_2$" high, signed Czechoslovakia.

684. Covered candy dish, 7$^1/_2$" wide, unknown maker.

685. "Venus Rising" figurine, 6$^1/_2$" high, marked IG-81, made in 1981 for Mirror Images by Imperial Glass Company using the old Cambridge mold (No. 518). Less than 1,000 of these pieces were made.

686. Handblown swan figurine, 4$^3/_4$" high, with label, Big Pine Key Glassworks (FL) circa 1970s.

687. "Sonny Boy" figurine, 4" high, marked "Sonny Boy Our Gang," R. Wetzel Glass for Our Gang Collectors 1981. This figurine was a trial piece, and was not sold as a catalog item.

688. Indian Chief toothpick holder, 2$^1/_2$" high, marked V in a circle, Summit Art Glass circa 1980s.

689. "Wise Ole' Owl" figurine, 3$^3/_4$" high, marked with a D in a heart, made by Degenhart's Crystal Art Glass of Cambridge, Ohio circa 1960s.

690. Horse's head stopper, 3$^3/_4$" high, marked with a B, unknown maker circa 1970s.

691. "Sammy Rodeo Clown" figurine, 4$^1/_4$" high, marked with t in a teardrop, made by Botson's Machine & Mold for Turner's Treasure Glass 1981. Rare in black glass.

692. Handblown cat figurine, 4" high to top of

tail, with label, Pilgrim Glass Corp. of Ceredo, West Virginia 1987.

693. Handblown horse figurine, 5" high, with label, Pilgrim Glass Corporation 1987.

694. Handblown pig figurine, 4" long, with label, Pilgrim Glass Corporation 1987.

695. Handblown panther figurine, 6" long, with label, Pilgrim Glass Corporation 1987.

696. Whale figurine, 4" long, 2$^1/_2$" high, Pilgrim Glass Corporation 1987.

697. Snail figurine, 4" high, 4" long, Pilgrim Glass Corporation 1987.

698. 7$^1/_4$" wastebasket, decorated with a bead of white glass swirled around the sides, with label, Pilgrim Glass Corporation 1987.

699A–C. Handblown flower stems, ranging from 8" to 10" long, unknown maker circa 1980s.

700. Handblown angel figurine, 2" high, crystal halo and wings, unknown maker circa 1980s.

701. Handblown Madonna figurine, 9" high, unknown maker circa 1980s.

702. Horse figurine, 5$^1/_2$" high, marked M for Mosser Glass Company of Cambridge, Ohio circa 1980s.

703. No. 173 Bird figurine, 3" long, marked with M, Mosser Glass Company circa 1980s.

704. Rabbit figurine, 5$^1/_4$" long, marked with M, Mosser Glass Company circa 1980s.

705. Mini Jenny Doll, 2$^1/_8$" high, marked with H, for Vi Hunter by Mosser Glass 1981.

706. Jenny Doll figurine, 4" high, marked with H, made for Vi Hunter by Mosser Glass 1981.

707. Hen covered dish, milk glass head, 6$^1/_2$" wide, Mosser Glass Company circa 1980s.

708. Camel covered dish, 6" wide, marked with WG indicating it was made in the Westmoreland mold, Rosso's Wholesale Glass circa 1980s.

709. 2" miniature bunny figurine, unknown maker circa 1980s.

710. "Charlotte Doll" figurine, 4^1/$_2$" high, marked with keystone R, made in Westmoreland mold, Rosso's Wholesale Glass 1981.

711. 7" basket, Mary Gregory decoration, marked with keystone R, made in the Westmoreland mold, Rosso's Wholesale Glass 1992.

712. Squirrel toothpick holder, 2^1/$_4$" high, Rosso's Wholesale Glass circa 1980s.

713. Bird in Flight figurine, 8^1/$_2$" high to tail, Rosso's Wholesale Glass circa 1980s.

714. Bulldog figurine 2^1/$_2$" high, marked with keystone R, made in Westmoreland mold (their Line No. 75), Rosso's Wholesale Glass 1992.

715. 7" basket, Mary Gregory decoration, marked with keystone R, made in the Westmoreland mold, Rosso's Wholesale Glass 1992.

716. "Bottoms Up" glass, woman lying over dome of cup, 3^1/$_4$" high, Guernsey Glass Company of Cambridge, Ohio 1979.

717. Rabbit decorator plate, 8" wide, marked with WG indicating it was made in the original Westmoreland mold, for Rosso's Wholesale Glass circa 1980s.

718. Open lace candlesticks, 5" high, made in old Westmoreland mold for Rosso's Wholesale Glass 1992.

719. Open lace console bowl, 9" wide, made in old Westmoreland mold for Rosso's Wholesale Glass 1992.

720. 7" basket with Mary Gregory decoration, marked with keystone R, made in the Westmoreland mold, Rosso's Wholesale Glass 1992.

721. Measuring cup with reamer top, Rosso's Wholesale Glass 1987.

722. Reamer, 4^1/$_2$" diameter, marked EASLEY'S

PAT. JULY 10, 1888 & SEPT. 10, 1889, Rosso's Wholesale Glass 1987.

723. 2-cup juice pitcher with reamer top, Rosso's Wholesale Glass 1987.

724. Turtle figurine, 5^1/$_4$" long, 2" high, marked with AB, made by Botson's Machine & Mold, Rosso's Wholesale Glass circa 1980s.

725. Miniature butter dish, inverted strawberry pattern, 4^3/$_4$" diameter, marked with AB, made by Botson's Machine & Mold, Rosso's Wholesale Glass circa 1980s.

726. 2^1/$_4$" Civil War mug, marked with AB, made by Botson's Machine & Mold, Rosso's Wholesale Glass circa 1982.

727. Toothpick holder, Frog carrying seashell, 2^1/$_2$" high, 3^1/$_2$" long, reproduction marked with keystone R, Rosso's Wholesale Glass circa 1980s.

728. Small vase, 4^1/$_2$" high, marked with AB, made by Botson's Machine & Mold, Rosso's Wholesale Glass circa 1980s.

729. Toothpick holder, inverted strawberry pattern, 2^1/$_2$" high, marked with AB, made by Botson's Machine & Mold for Rosso's Wholesale Glass circa 1980s.

730. "Clyde" rocking horse figurine, 3^1/$_2$" high, marked AB, made by Botson's Machine & Mold, Rosso's Wholesale Glass circa 1980s.

731. Reamer, 7" wide, Rosso's Wholesale Glass circa 1980s.

732. Rabbit covered dish, 9" long, made in old Imperial Glass mold, Rosso's Wholesale Glass circa 1980s.

733. Turtle cigarette box, 7^1/$_2$" long, Rosso's Wholesale Glass 1991. This piece was made in the original Westmoreland mold. So few reproductions were made that the value is almost as high as that of the original box.

734. Heart-shaped salt dip, 2" long, Rosso's Wholesale Glass circa 1980s.

735. Candlesticks, Maple Leaf pattern (West-

moreland's Line No. 1928), 5^1/$_8$" high, marked WG indicating it was made in the original Westmoreland mold, Rosso's Wholesale Glass 1992.

736. "Wise Ole' Owl" figurine, 3^3/$_4$" high, marked with D in a heart, Degenhart's Crystal Art Glass of Cambridge, Ohio circa 1960s.

737. Console bowl, Maple Leaf pattern (Westmoreland's Line No. 1928), 10" wide, marked WG indicating it was made in the original Westmoreland mold, Rosso's Wholesale Glass 1992.

738. Train engine car, 2^1/$_2$" high, 4^1/$_4$" long, marked with AB, made by Botson's Machine & Mold, Rosso's Wholesale Glass 1982.

739. Lady ashtray, 9" long, Rosso's Wholesale Glass circa 1980s. This piece is a reproduction of Westmoreland's Line No. 456 Ballerina mint dish or ashtray. Again, so few reproductions were made that I have priced them as high as the originals.

MOSSER GLASS COMPANY AND OTHERS, P. 59

Mosser Glass, Inc. of Cambridge, Ohio made opaque black glass circa 1981–83. Established in the 1960s, Mosser Glass primarily manufactured novelty items and tableware.

740. No. 177 Audubon Cardinal figurine, 5^1/$_2$" high, marked with M, Mosser Glass 1981–83.

741. No. 193 Collie figurine, 3^1/$_8$" high, marked with M, Mosser Glass 1981–83.

742. Owl figurine, black satin, 4^3/$_4$" high, marked with M, Mosser Glass 1981–83.

743. Owl figurine, black satin with glass eyes, 4" high, marked with M, Mosser Glass 1981–83.

744. Owl figurine, 4^3/$_4$" high, marked with M, Mosser Glass 1981–83.

745. Bear figurine, 3^3/$_4$" high, marked with M, Mosser Glass 1981–83.

746. Duck covered dish, milk glass head, 5" long, unmarked, Mosser Glass 1981–83.

747. No. 194 Cat figurine, 4" long, marked with M, Mosser Glass 1981–83.

748. Squirrel figurine, black satin, 2" high, marked with M, Mosser Glass 1981–83.

749. Frog figurine, black satin, 2" high, marked with M, Mosser Glass 1981–83.

750. Squirrel figurine, 2" high, marked with M, Mosser Glass 1981–83.

751. No. 194 Cat figurine, black satin, 4" long, marked with M, Mosser Glass 1981–83.

752. Frog figurine with glass eyes, 3" high, 4" long, marked with M, Mosser Glass Co. 1981–83.

753. Flower bowl, unknown maker circa 1980s.

754. Liberty bell, 5^1/$_2$" high, marked with M, Mosser Glass 1981–83.

755. No. 1921 4^1/$_2$" compote, Lotus pattern, marked WG, Westmoreland Glass Company circa 1970s.

756. Daisy & Button slipper, 6" long, 2^1/$_2$" high, unknown maker circa 1980s.

757. Picture frame, 7^1/$_2$" high, 5^1/$_2$" wide, Mikasa of Japan circa 1980s.

758. 2-piece flower bowl, 7" wide, 2^1/$_2$" high, Lotus pattern, unmarked, Westmoreland Glass Company circa 1970s.

759. Daisy & Button hat, 2^1/$_2$" high, unknown maker circa 1980s.

760. Pressed toothpick holder, 2^3/$_4$" high, unknown maker circa 1980s.

761. Elephant figurine, 4^1/$_2$" long, 3^1/$_2$" high, unmarked, Mosser Glass 1981–83.

762. One-light candlestick, 2^3/$_4$" high, unknown maker circa 1980s.

763. Toothpick holder with strawberry pattern,

2¹/₂" high, Guernsey Glass Company of Cambridge, Ohio circa 1980s.

764. Bird dish, 6" long, unknown maker circa 1980s.

765. Pressed bowl, diamond pattern, 6" wide, unknown maker circa 1980s.

766. Salt and pepper shakers, 3" high, unknown maker circa 1970s.

767. Footed console bowl, 12" wide, 4¹/₂" high, unknown maker circa 1980s.

768. Flower bowl, 5" high, 4¹/₂" diameter, unknown maker circa 1980s.

ONEIDA CRYSTAL AND OTHERS, P. 60

Figures 769–774 were purchased from Oneida Crystal Corporation of New York. Oneida's crystal ware is made in Germany and Korea, among other locations.

769. Right and left high-heeled shoes, 4¹/₂" long, with label, Oneida Crystal 1991.

770. Seal figurine, 3" long, with label, Oneida Crystal 1991.

771. Fish figurine, 4" long, with label, Oneida Crystal 1991.

772. Rabbit figurine, 2¹/₂" high, with label, Oneida Crystal 1991.

773. Teddy Bear figurine, 3" high, with label, Oneida Crystal 1991.

774. Turtle figurine, 4" long, with label, Oneida Crystal 1991.

775. Perfume atomizer with decorative stopper, 4¹/₂" diameter, with label, made in Taiwan circa 1970s.

776. Lotion dispenser, plastic top, 3¹/₂" high, with label, made in Taiwan circa 1970s.

777. House-shaped bottle, 3" high, unknown maker.

778. 2" decorative mushroom, Fenton Art Glass Company 1991.

779. 4" Candle Scents (holds scented or votive candles), made in Taiwan for Beacon Hill circa 1980s.

780. Die-shaped cologne bottle, plastic stopper, 3¹/₄" high, marked "AD," made for Alfred Dunhill.

781. Jupiter Train cologne bottle, 5¹/₂" high, made for Stanley Home Products.

782. Mini Bunny salt, 1¹/₂" high, made for E & E Collectables circa 1980s.

783. Square 4-footed trinket box, handpainted decoration, 2¹/₂" wide, 2³/₄" high, marked WG, Westmoreland Glass Company circa 1980s. Decorated by Rosso's Wholesale Glass. This piece was Westmoreland's No. 275 Victorian trinket box.

784. Mini Hen salt, 1¹/₂" high, made for E & E Collectables circa 1980s.

785A. Lacy Daisy berry bowl, part of a set that comes with four miniature bowls, 4¹/₄" diameter, Summit Art Glass 1988–89.

785B. Lacy Daisy miniature berry bowl, 2¹/₄" diameter, Summit Art Glass 1988–89.

786A. Lotus berry bowl, part of a set that comes with four miniature bowls, 4" diameter, marked with V in a circle, Summit Art Glass 1988–89.

786B. Lotus miniature berry bowl, 1¹/₂" diameter, marked with V in a circle, Summit Art Glass 1988–89.

787A. Caprice berry bowl, part of a set that comes with four miniature bowls, 4¹/₂" diameter, Summit Art Glass 1988–89.

787B. Caprice miniature berry bowl, 2¹/₂" diameter, Summit Art Glass 1988–89.

PERFUME BOTTLES AND ATOMIZERS, PP. 61–63

788. 3 oz. spray perfume, for Jean-Charles Brosseau, Ombre Rose perfume, made in Paris circa 1980s.

789. 1 oz. spray perfume, for Jean-Charles Brosseau, Ombre Rose perfume, made in Paris circa 1980s.

790. Candy kiss atomizer, unknown maker circa 1990s.

791. 1 oz. perfume, made for DeN Beauty Counselors Inc. Dist.

792. Hand-cut round perfume, made in Japan, Irving Rice (Irice) 1985–86.

793. Hand-cut tall perfume bottle, made in Japan, Irice 1985–86.

794. Hand-cut round perfume, black satin, made in Japan, Irice 1985–86.

795. Spray perfume, made in Japan, for Irice 1985–86.

796. Round perfume with butterfly stopper, black satin, made in Japan, Irice circa 1980s.

797. Spray perfume, unknown maker.

798. 1/10 oz. sample perfume, made for Mary Quant Cosmetics, England.

799. Perfume with heart stopper, black satin, made in Japan, Irice 1985–86.

800. 1/8 oz. Lips perfume, Salvador Dali design, 1990.

801. Perfume with tulip stopper, black satin, made in Japan, Irice 1985–86.

802. Made for Sculptura Perfume, Jovan, Inc. of Chicago, Illinois 1981.

803. Round perfume with ball dauber, made in Japan, Irice circa 1980s.

804. Atomizer, black satin, made in Japan, Irice 1985–86.

805. Atomizer, made for Marcel Franck, Paris circa 1980s.

806. Tall atomizer, unknown maker.

807. Spray perfume, made in Japan for Irice 1985–86.

808. Perfume with decorative stopper, black satin, made in Japan, Irice 1985–86.

809. Atomizer, made in Japan, Irice 1985–86.

810. Atomizer, for Nat Robbins, New York circa 1980s.

811. Atomizer, black satin, made in Japan, Irice circa 1980s.

812. Pocketbook spray perfume, made in Japan, Irice circa 1980s.

813. Factice bottle, used only for display, made in France for Maxim's De Paris 1986. This bottle was actually donated by Maxim's for illustration in this book!

814. 1/10 oz. perfume, made in France for Maxim's De Paris 1986.

815. Spray perfume, made in Japan, Irice 1985–86.

816. Atomizer, made in Japan, Irice 1985–86.

817. Hand-cut atomizer, made in Japan, Irice 1985–86.

818. 1/3 oz. sachet jar, made for Avon Collectibles circa 1980s.

819. No. 1902 dresser set with 4$\frac{1}{2}$" bottles, 4" puff box and 10" tray, marked WG, Westmoreland Glass Company circa 1970s. Westmoreland made this set in other colors and decorations intermittently from 1971 until the factory closed in 1984, but the black set was experimental, and never sold through the company's catalog.

820. Triangular spray perfume, made in Japan circa 1980s.

821. 1/4 oz. perfume, for Jean-Charles Brosseau, Ombre Rose perfume, made in Paris circa 1980s.

822. Factice cologne, used only for display, made for Musk Cologne, by Monsieur Houbigant.

823. 1 oz. cologne, made for Musk Cologne, by Monsieur Houbigant.

824. 3 oz. cologne, black glass with added silver sheen, made for Xeryus Cologne, by Givenchy of Paris circa 1980s.

825. 1/5 oz. cologne, black glass with added silver sheen, made for Xeryus Cologne, by Givenchy of Paris circa 1980s.

826. 7 ml. cologne, made for Van Cleef Arpels of Paris.

827. 1/5 oz. cologne, made for Drakkar Noir Cologne, Paris circa 1980s.

828. 8 oz. cologne, made for Musk Cologne, by Monsieur Houbigant, New York.

829. Factice bottle, used only for display, made for Bob Macky Perfume 1986. This bottle was also donated by Bob Macky for illustration in this book!

830. Handblown perfume with black and milk glass stopper, $9^3/_4$" high, stopper is $9^1/_2$" long, with label, made for Bruns, U. S. A.

831. Crystal perfume with black stopper, called "Geneva" from the No. 15 Vanity Set, New Martinsville Glass Company 1932.

832. Cased crystal over black perfume and stopper, with label, made in Taiwan circa 1990s.

833. Oval perfume, black carnival, with label, made in Taiwan circa 1990s.

834. Perfume, black carnival, with label, made in Taiwan circa 1990s.

835. Heart perfume, black satin, with label, made in Taiwan circa 1990s.

836. Black glass perfume with metal design, with label, made in Morocco circa 1990s.

837. Black glass perfume with metal design, with label, made in Morocco circa 1990s.

838. Atomizer, black satin and opaque black, with label, made in France circa 1990s.

839. Perfume, with label, Oneida Crystal Corporation circa 1990s.

840. Atomizer, black satin, with label, made in France circa 1990s.

841. Crystal perfume with black stopper, Punch pattern, L. E. Smith Glass Company 1932.

842. Atomizer, black and milk spatter glass, with label, made in Italy circa 1990s.

843. No. 153 perfume with milk glass stopper, Imperial Glass Corporation circa 1930s–40s.

844. Atomizer in metal holder, with label, made in Japan circa 1990s.

845. Octagonal atomizer, with label, made in France circa 1990s.

846. Vanity set with atomizers, jar and tray, black satin, with label, made in Taiwan circa 1990s.

847. Puff box, $3^1/_2$" wide, 3" high, also made with a yellow lid, Akro Agate Company Clarksburg, West Virginia circa 1930s.

848. Square powder box, unknown maker circa 1930s. This box was made in amber and crystal, as well as black, and the manufacturer often matched colors

849. Crystal puff box with black glass cover, called "Judy" but pattern name not known, New Martinsville Glass Company circa 1930s.

850. Vanity set with atomizer, jar and leaf-shaped tray, black satin, with label, made in Taiwan circa 1990s.

851. Perfume in silver casing, made in France circa 1990s.

852. Perfume, made in France circa 1930s–40s.

853. Perfume in metal casing, with label, made in Taiwan circa 1990s.

854. Perfume decorated with gold filigree and glass beads, coral stopper with carved rose, signed Czechoslovakia circa early 1900s.

855. 1/4 oz. perfume, made for Jean-Charles Brosseau, Ombre Rose perfume, made in Paris circa 1980s.

856. Black Crystal perfume with faceted stopper, unknown maker circa 1990s.

857. Crystal powder box with black lid, Sunset pattern, Paden City Glass Company 1936.

858. No. 18/2 crystal powder box with black lid, part of the Crystal Eagle line, New Martinsville Glass Company circa 1930s.

859. Round powder box missing original cover, unknown maker circa 1930s.

PLATES, P. 64

860. 8" plate, Forget-Me-Not border and Mary Gregory decoration, marked WG, Westmoreland Glass Company circa 1950s.

861. 7¼" plate, possibly a later reproduction of Kemple Glassworks' No. 42 101-Open Edge plate, 8½" diameter, which was actually made in an older mold purchased from Mannington Art Glass in 1944–45. While Kemple did not make black glass, this plate was apparently made from their mold.

862. 8" plate, Forget-Me-Not border and Mary Gregory decoration, marked WG, Westmoreland Glass Company circa 1950s.

863. 5½" plate with Gothic border, Canton Glass Company mold, made by Westmoreland circa 1920s. This plate came in six sizes.

864. Serving platter, 18½" diameter, unknown maker.

865. Cup plate with Indian head, 3" diameter, Summit Art Glass circa 1980s.

866. Rabbit decorator plate, 8" wide, marked with WG indicating it was made in the original Westmoreland mold, for Rosso's Wholesale Glass circa 1980s.

867. 8½" plate with Wicket border, Atterbury & Company mold, made by Westmoreland Glass Company circa 1920s.

868. George Washington Bicentennial plate (1732–1932), 8¼" diameter, L. E. Smith Glass Company 1932.

STANDS, P. 65

Figures 869–896 were manufactured by a variety of companies. In most cases, it is very hard to determine the maker. However, many of them were made during the Depression era as display bases to highlight the new and exciting colors of elegant glassware.

869. Footed stand, 4½" wide, Beaumont Glass Company circa 1920s.

870. Dolphin stand, 6" wide, unknown maker.

871. Dolphin stand, black satin, 6" wide, unknown maker.

872. 5-legged ebony pedestal, 4¾" wide, Fenton Art Glass Company circa 1930s.

873. Footed stand, 3" diameter, unknown maker circa 1920s–30s.

874. Footed stand, 4" diameter, unknown maker circa 1920s–30s.

875. Footed stand, 4½" diameter, Fenton Art Glass Company circa 1920s–30s.

876. Footed stand, 3¾" diameter, unknown maker circa 1920s–30s.

877. Footed stand, 3½" diameter, unknown maker circa 1920s–30s.

878. Footed stand, 4" diameter, unknown maker circa 1920s–30s.

879. Footed stand, 4½" diameter, unknown maker circa 1920s–30s.

880. Footed stand, 5" diameter, unknown maker circa 1920s–30s.

881. Footed stand, 4" diameter, unknown maker circa 1920s–30s.

882. Footed stand, 4" diameter, unknown maker circa 1920s–30s.

883. Footed stand, 3" diameter, Fenton Art Glass Company circa 1920s–30s.

884. Footed stand, 4" diameter, unknown maker, circa 1920s–30s.

885. Footed stand, unknown maker circa 1920s–30s.

886. Round stand, used for seating console bowls, black satin with gold trim, 3¹⁄₈" diameter, Tiffin Glass (U. S. Glass Factory R) circa 1920s–30s.

887. Footed stand, black satin, 3" diameter, Tiffin Glass (U. S. Glass Factory R) circa 1920s–30s.

888. Footed stand, 6" diameter, unknown maker circa 1920s–30s.

889. Round stand with sea lions and pedestal, 3" diameter, unknown maker circa 1920s–30s. This stand originally supported a small crystal rose bowl.

890. Hurricane holder with loop handle, 5" diameter, Fenton Art Glass Company 1953–54. This originally held the No. 7398 Black Rose hurricane lamp, which was cased milk glass over pink, with black ruffled trim.

891. Footed stand, 4¹⁄₂" diameter, unknown maker circa 1920s–30s.

892. Punch bowl stand, 7" diameter, unknown maker circa 1920s–30s.

893. Footed stand, 4" diameter, unknown maker circa 1920s–30s.

894. No. 1031/0 flower bowl stand, 3" diameter, Westmoreland Glass Company circa 1920s.

895. Footed stand, 3" diameter, unknown maker circa 1920s–30s.

896. Footed punch bowl stand, 8" diameter, unknown maker circa 1920s–30s.

STEMWARE AND SMOKING ITEMS, P. 66

897. 8 oz. goblet, green glass on black glass base, unknown maker circa 1920s–30s.

898. 16 oz. iced tea glass, Libbey Glass Company circa 1990s.

899. 1 oz. cordial, crystal glass on black base, unknown maker circa 1920s–30s.

900. 4 oz. wine, crystal glass on black base, unknown maker circa 1920s–30s.

901. 8 oz. goblet, crystal glass on black base, unknown maker circa 1920s–30s.

902. Square 4 oz. wine, crystal on black base, marked "Di Saronno" and sold as a promotional piece with Di Saronno Wine.

903. 8 oz. rocks glass, crystal on black base, unknown maker.

904. 2 oz. "Bottoms Up" glass on black coaster, made in France circa 1920s–30s.

905. 12 oz. goblet, crystal on black scalloped base, black knop in stem, unknown maker circa 1920s–30s.

906. 4 oz. champagne goblet, crystal on black scalloped base, black knop in stem, unknown maker circa 1920s–30s.

907A–D. 1 oz. wine glasses, each cup in a different pastel color on twisted black stem with gold trim, made in France circa 1920s–30s.

908. 16 oz. "Ten Pin" pilsener, crystal glass on black base, Imperial Glass Corporation 1931.

909. Chrome cigarette holder on 7" black glass tray, unknown maker circa 1930s.

910. 6¹⁄₂" tobacco jar with wooden lid and pipe holder, pipe holder with label reading "Syracco Wood Syracuse, New York," unknown maker circa 1930s.

911. 3" cigarette holder, unknown maker circa 1920s–30s.

912. Ashtray with gold glitter, 3" diameter, made in Italy circa 1920s–30s.

913. Ashtray with design of a pipe and tobacco bag, 7¹⁄₄" long, 5" wide, made for the Houze Company circa 1920s–30s. This tray is missing a lighter that fits in the three small holes.

MADE IN TAIWAN, PP. 67–70

914. Footed vase, 11¹⁄₂" high, with label, circa 1980s.

915. Round vase, 4" high, black satin, with label, circa 1980s.

916. Hat pin holder, 7" high, imported circa 1980s.

917. Stemmed vase, black satin, $13^1/4$" high, with label, circa 1980s.

918. Egg with etched roses, black satin, 3" high, with label, 1992.

919. Stemmed vase, black satin, $7^1/2$" high, with label, circa 1980s.

920. Egg with etched swan, black satin, 3" high, with label, 1992.

921. Stemmed vase, black satin, $10^1/4$" high, with label, circa 1980s.

922. Pillar vase, black satin, $9^1/2$" high, with label, circa 1980s.

923. Black satin bird on crystal pin dish, $3^1/4$" diameter, with label, circa 1970s.

924. Whale figurine, 4" long, 3" high, with label, circa 1980s.

925. Lovebirds covered candy dish, $7^1/2$" high, 7" diameter, with label, 1989.

926. Musical notes bell, 4" high, with label, Enesco Company circa 1990s.

927. Figural fish, handblown, $4^1/2$" high, with label, circa 1990s.

928. Fluted vase, 11" high, with label, circa 1980s.

929. 10" footed vase with painted decoration, with label, circa 1980s.

930. Figural fish, handblown, $2^3/4$" high, with label, circa 1990s.

931. Footed vase with painted decoration, 10" high, with label, circa 1980s.

932. 5" square basket with basketweave pattern, with label, circa 1990s.

933. 1" crystal thimble with black glass notes, with label, circa 1980s.

934. 10" footed vase with painted decoration, with label, circa 1980s.

935. Figural fish, handblown, $2^3/4$" high, with label, circa 1990s.

936. 10" footed vase with painted decoration, with label, circa 1980s.

937. Winged Pegasus music box, 6" high, with label, circa 1980s.

938. Winged Pegasus music box, $6^1/2$" high, with label, circa 1980s.

939. Winged Pegasus music box, 7" high, with label, circa 1980s.

940. Frosted vase with black satin butterfly, $4^3/4$" high, with label, circa 1980s.

941. Fluted vase, black satin, 6" high, with label, circa 1980s.

942. Black satin vase with frosted bird, $3^3/4$" high, with label, circa 1980s.

943. Unicorn music box, 7" high, with label, circa 1980s.

944. Winged Pegasus music box, $6^1/2$" high, with label, circa 1980s.

945. Unicorn music box, 5" high, with label, circa 1980s.

946. Ruffled vase, black satin, 7" high, with label, circa 1980s.

947. Figural swan, $5^1/2$" high, with label, circa 1980s.

948–954. Multi-shaped vases, all $5^1/2$" high, all with label, made for Two's Company circa 1980s.

955. Figural swan, $4^1/2$" high, with label, circa 1980s.

956. Hurricane lamp, crystal shade on black base, $7^3/4$" high, with label, circa 1980s.

957. Black satin vase, $4^1/2$" high, with label, circa 1980s.

958. Scented oil lamp, $3^3/_4$" high, with label, made for Balos Company circa 1980s.

959. Scented oil lamp, $3^1/_2$" high, with label, made for Balos Company circa 1980s.

960. Figural swan, $6^3/_4$" high, with label, made for Crowning Touch circa 1980s.

961. Figural swan, $6^3/_4$" high, with label, made for Crowning Touch circa 1980s.

962. Black satin snail on crystal dish, $4^1/_2$" diameter, circa 1980s.

963. Lily vase, black satin, 5" high, with label, circa 1980s.

964. Ball vase, 4" diameter, with label, circa 1980s.

965. Ruffled vase, black satin, $10^1/_2$" high, with label, circa 1980s.

966. Figural fish, handblown, $3^1/_2$" high, $6^1/_2$" long, with label, circa 1990s.

967. Figural fish, handblown, $2^3/_4$" high, $4^1/_2$" long, with label, circa 1990s.

968. 2-piece Rooster covered dish, $8^1/_2$" high, with label, circa 1980s.

969. Globe paperweight, black satin, $2^1/_2$" diameter, with label, circa 1990s.

970. Siamese Cat figurine, 4" long, 2" high, with label, made for Crowning Touch circa 1980s.

971. Majestic Cat figurine, $6^1/_4$" high, with label, circa 1980s.

972. Robin on Nest covered dish, 5" wide, marked "Taiwan" circa 1980s.

973. Bottle, $4^1/_2$" high, with label, made for Two's Company circa 1980s.

974. Top hat, black satin, 2" high, with label, circa 1980s.

975. Ball vase, 6" diameter, with label, made for Two's Company circa 1980s.

976. Bird figurine, crystal with black swirls, $4^1/_2$" long, 3" high, with label, circa 1980s.

977. Bird figurine, 4" long, 2" high, with label, circa 1980s.

978. Hen on Nest covered dish, black satin, 6" wide, marked "Taiwan" circa 1980s.

979. Vase, $7^1/_4$" high, with label, made for Two's Company circa 1980s.

980. Round vase, $3^3/_4$" diameter, with label, made for Two's Company circa 1980s.

981. 6" bell with crystal handle, with label, circa 1970s.

982. Heart with swirl pattern, $3^1/_2$" wide, with label, made for Toyo Co. circa 1990s.

983. High boot, 4" high, marked "Taiwan" 1991.

984. Figural bird, handblown with gold trim, $3^1/_4$" high, with label, circa 1980s.

985. Figural cat, handblown with gold trim, $3^1/_2$" high, with label, circa 1980s.

986. Oil lamp, 5" high, 9" high with shade, marked "Taiwan" circa 1970s.

987. Pillar vase, black satin, 9" high, with label, circa 1980s.

988. Tall vase, $10^1/_2$" high, with label, made for Balos Company circa 1990s.

989. A-shaped vase, black satin, 12" high, marked "Balos Taiwan" circa 1990s.

990. Twisted candlestick, 6" high, with label, circa 1990s.

991. Oval vase, black satin and opaque, 12" high, with label, circa 1990s.

992. Pressed bottle with flower design, 8" high, with label, circa 1990s.

993. Pressed bottle with flower design, $6^3/_4$" high, with label, circa 1990s.

994. Pressed bottle with flower design, $4^1/_2$" high, with label, circa 1990s.

995–999. Assorted bottles of different shapes with etched design, ranging from 2¹/₂" to 4¹/₂" high, all with label, circa 1990s.

1000. Iridized vase, mouthblown to resemble sandcarving, 6" high, with label, Silvestri Corporation circa 1990s.

1001. 5" flower vase, with label, circa 1990s.

1002. Figural whale, black carnival, 7" long, with label, circa 1990s.

1003. Figural fish, black carnival, 4¹/₂" long, with label, made in Hawaii, Pele's Glass circa 1990s.

1004. Scented oil lamp, 3¹/₂" high, with label, Balos Company circa 1980s.

1005. Scented oil lamp, 3³/₄" high, with label, Balos Company circa 1980s.

1006–1010. Perfume bottles, all black satin, ranging from 2¹/₂" to 2³/₄" high, with label, circa 1990s.

1011. Ball vase, 4¹/₂" diameter, with label, circa 1990s.

1012. Vanity tray, black satin, 5¹/₂" long, with label, circa 1990s.

TAIWAN AND OTHER IMPORTS, P. 71

1013. Two-light candlestick, 5" high, made in Taiwan circa 1990s.

1014. Footed flower bowl, 4¹/₂" high, 5" diameter, made in Taiwan circa 1990s.

1015. Lovebirds covered dish, 7¹/₂" high, 7" diameter, with label, made in Taiwan 1989.

1016. Bird flower holder, 5¹/₂" high, with label, made in Taiwan circa 1990s.

1017. One-light candlestick with loop handle, 3" high, with label, circa 1990s.

1018. 14 oz. pilsener, with label, made in China 1996.

1019. 4 oz. wine, crystal glass on black stem and base, with label, made in France circa 1990s.

1020. 6 oz. wine, crystal glass on black stem and base, with label, made in France circa 1990s.

1021. 4 oz. wine, crystal glass on black stem and base, with label, made in France circa 1990s.

1022. 4 oz. wine, crystal glass on black stem and base, with label, made in France, Luminarc circa 1990s.

1023. 6 oz. wine, crystal glass on black stem and base, with label, made in France circa 1990s.

1024. Luncheon plate, 8" diameter, marked "France" circa 1990s.

1025. 6¹/₂" vase, with label, Mikasa of Japan circa 1990s.

1026. 6 oz. glass, black satin with rose design, made in Japan, Irice circa 1990s.

1027. Figural fish, cased crystal over green and black glass, 3¹/₂" high, with label, made in Taiwan circa 1990s.

1028. 5 oz. wine glass with flower design, unknown maker. This piece is also shown inverted to better illustrate the pattern.

TIARA EXCLUSIVES, PP. 72–74

Figures 1029–1062 are all labeled "Tiara Glass," and were manufactured by the Indiana Glass Company (division of Lancaster Colony) for this line of reproduction tableware from 1978 through the 1980s.

1029. Footed candlesticks, 3¹/₄" wide, 4¹/₄" high, Sawtooth or Cameo pattern.

1030. 8 oz. tumbler, Sawtooth or Cameo pattern.

1031. Stemmed candy dish with cover, 12" high, Sawtooth or Cameo pattern.

1032. Salt and pepper shakers with chrome lids, 4" high, Sawtooth or Cameo pattern.

1033. Stemmed candy dish with cover, 17" high, Sawtooth or Cameo pattern.

1034. 11" basket, Miranda pattern.

1035. Covered honey dish, Beehive pattern, 6" high, 6" wide.

1036. 8 oz. German beer stein, 6" high.

1037. 8 oz. Hunter's Horn mug.

1038. Colonial candy box and cover, 5³/₄" high.

1039. Canister with floral pattern, 7¹/₄" high.

1040. Canister with floral pattern, 5⁵/₈" high.

1041. Canister with floral pattern, 8⁷/₈" high.

1042. Regal salad bowl, 10" diameter, 4¹/₂" high.

1043. Double spout water pitcher, holds 1¹/₂ quarts.

1044. Regal 3-sided bowl, 10" wide.

1045A–B. Monarch 4" handled sugar and 4³/₄" creamer.

1046. Monarch candlesticks, 5" diameter.

1047. Monarch covered butter dish, earlier made by Indiana Glass Company as their No. 123.

1048. Regal bowl, 8" diameter, 11" high.

1049. 8 oz. goblet, unknown maker.

1050. 8 oz. Powder Horn tumbler.

1051. 8 oz. tumbler, Hobnail pattern.

1052. 1¹/₂ quart pitcher, Hobnail pattern.

1053. 10" basket, Sawtooth or Cameo pattern.

1054. Console bowl, Sawtooth or Cameo pattern, 9³/₄" diameter.

1055. Ruffled console bowl, 9" diameter.

1056. Buffet divided relish tray, 10" long.

1057. 32 oz. covered candy box, Weiss pattern.

1058. "Pyramid" handled relish tray, 8" wide.

1059. 12 oz. "Pyramid" tumbler.

1060. 6" ashtray, Sawtooth or Cameo pattern.

1061. Special 1982 Tiara Glass Convention plate, scalloped edge and eagle design with the words "Soar To New Heights," 8" diameter.

1062. 6" basket, Hobnail pattern.

TIFFIN OR U. S. GLASS, P. 75

Incorporated in 1888 by A. J. Beatty, Tiffin Glass (of Tiffin, Ohio) primarily manufactured quality tableware and glass barware. In 1892, Tiffin joined the U. S. Glass Company, operating as Factory R until 1963. Tiffin made its opaque black and black satin colors intermittently from 1922 through the early 1970s. Figures 1067–1075 represent glass made by Tiffin during its tenure as "Factory R."

1063. Black satin vase, 9¹/₂" high, unknown maker circa 1920s–30s.

1064. Black satin bud vase with gold decoration, 10¹/₄" high, unknown maker circa 1920s–30s.

1065. Black satin bud vase with painted decoration, 8" high, unknown maker circa 1920s–30s.

1066. Footed black satin vase with gold trim, 8" high, unknown maker circa 1920s–30s.

1067. Square vase, black satin with sandcarved nudes design, 9¹/₂" high, Tiffin Glass (U. S. Glass Factory R) 1924–34.

1068. No. 9448 Large Cat, black satin with painted facial features, 11" high, Tiffin Glass (U. S. Glass Factory R) 1924–34.

1069. Bulb box, Elysium pattern with dancing ladies around the sides, made in both opaque and satin, 10" long, 4" wide, 4" high, Tiffin Glass (U. S. Glass Factory R) 1924–34.

1070. 2" square candlestick, black satin, Tiffin Glass (U. S. Glass Factory R) 1924–29.

1071. No. 63 pillar candlestick, 7¹/₂" high, black satin, Tiffin Glass (U. S. Glass Factory R) 1924–34.

1072. No. 319 handled candlestick, black satin, 2³/₄" high, Tiffin Glass (U. S. Glass Factory R) 1924–29.

1073. No. 69 Frog candlesticks, black satin, with original label painted in gold leaf, 5$\frac{1}{2}$" high, Tiffin Glass (U. S. Glass Factory R) 1924–34.

1074. Bathtub novelty, gold painting on the side reads "Souvenir of Kansas City," 5$\frac{1}{4}$" long, Tiffin Glass (U. S. Glass Factory R) 1924–36.

1075. Oval ashtray, black satin with raised design of Carnegie National Bank, 6" long, Tiffin Glass (U. S. Glass Factory R) 1928.

VIKING GLASS COMPANY AND DALZELL-VIKING, PP. 76–77

In 1944, the New Martinsville Glass Company of New Martinsville, West Virginia changed ownership to become Viking Glass (a name probably adapted from the heavy Swedish-type glassware the firm manufactured). Viking made black glass in 1950 and in the early 1980s. In 1986, the company closed and was reopened a year later as Dalzell-Viking Corporation, continuing its production of crystal and colored wares until closing in 1998.

1076. No. 4554 Fleur candlestick (formerly New Martinsville's No. 4500 Janice line), black satin, 5$\frac{1}{2}$" high, with label, Viking Glass Company circa 1980s.

1077. Spiral candlestick, made in old mold from Westmoreland Glass No. 1933 candlestick, 7" high, with label, Viking Glass Company circa 1980s.

1078. Swan console bowl (looks like a piece from New Martinsville's No. 4500 line), 11$\frac{3}{4}$" wide, with label, Viking Glass Co. circa 1980s.

1079. Swan console bowl (looks like a piece from New Martinsville's No. 4500 line), 6$\frac{3}{4}$" wide, with label, Viking Glass Co. circa 1980s.

1080. Handled serving tray with black satin Dolphin center, made in old mold from Westmoreland's No. 1049 tray, 11" diameter, with label, Viking Glass Company circa 1980s.

1081. No. 8566 Squirrel Tail candlestick, made from old Westmoreland mold, black satin, 6$\frac{3}{4}$" high, with label, Viking Glass Company circa 1980s.

1082. Horn candlestick, made from old Westmoreland mold, black satin, 4" high, with label, Viking Glass Company circa 1980s.

1083. No. 970 Classic candlestick, made from old Westmoreland mold, 4$\frac{1}{4}$" high, with label, Viking Glass Company circa 1980s.

1084. No. 8562 Dolphin candlesticks, made in old mold from Westmoreland's No. 1049 candlestick, 9" high, both with label, Viking Glass Company circa 1980s.

1085. No. 13 salt and pepper shakers, 3$\frac{3}{4}$" high, with label, Viking Glass Company circa 1980s.

1086. Ice bucket, 6$\frac{1}{2}$" high, with label, Viking Glass Company circa 1980s.

1087. No. 1140 bud vase, Epic pattern, 10" high, with label, Viking Glass Company circa 1980s.

1088. 6" covered candy dish with three Dolphin feet, black satin, Argonaut Shell pattern, made in old Westmoreland Glass mold from Line No. 1048, with label, Viking Glass Company circa 1980s.

1089. Bunny figurine, 2$\frac{1}{2}$" high, with label, Viking Glass Company circa 1980s.

1090. Fox figurine, 2$\frac{1}{2}$" high, with label, Viking Glass Company circa 1980s.

1091. No. 1311 Bird figurine, 10" high, with label, Viking Glass Company circa 1980s.

1092. No. 8252 Cat figurine, 2$\frac{1}{2}$" high, with label, Viking Glass Company circa 1980s.

1093. Teddy Bear figurine, 2$\frac{1}{2}$" high, with label, Viking Glass Company circa 1980s.

1094. No. 7926 cake salver, 12" diameter, with label, Viking Glass Company circa 1980s.

1095. Dog figurine, 2$\frac{1}{2}$" high, with label, Viking Glass Company circa 1980s.

1096. Owl figurine, 2$\frac{1}{2}$" high, with label, Viking Glass Company circa 1980s.

1097. No. 8563 Dolphin candlesticks, made in old mold from Westmoreland's No. 1049 candlestick, 4" high, with label, Viking Glass Company circa 1980s.

1098. Dolphin shell bowl, 8" wide, made in old mold from Westmoreland's No. 1049 footed shell bowl, with label, Viking Glass Company circa 1980s.

1099. No. 9105 Candlewick platter, 12" diameter, signed Dalzell, Dalzell-Viking 1990.

1100. No. 9101 Candlewick cup and saucer, signed Dalzell, Dalzell-Viking 1990.

1101. No. 9104 Candlewick dinner plate, 10" diameter, signed Dalzell, Dalzell-Viking 1990.

1102. No. 9103 Candlewick salad plate, 8" diameter, signed Dalzell, Dalzell-Viking 1990.

1103. No. 9102 Candlewick 6" dessert plate, signed Dalzell, Dalzell-Viking 1990.

1104. No. 488 Mama Bear figurine, 6" long, $4^1/_2$" high, signed Dalzell, Dalzell-Viking 1990.

1105. No. 716 Wolfhound figurine, 9" long, 7" high, signed Dalzell, Dalzell-Viking 1990.

1106. No. 5515 three-light candelabra, $6^1/_2$" long, $4^1/_2$" high, signed Dalzell, Dalzell-Viking 1990.

1107. No. 677 Squirrel figurine, $5^1/_2$" high, signed Dalzell, Dalzell-Viking 1990.

1108. No. 762 Pig figurine, $6^3/_4$" long, signed Dalzell, Dalzell-Viking 1990.

1109. No. 487 Baby Bear figurine, 5" long, $3^1/_4$" high, signed Dalzell, Dalzell-Viking 1990.

1110. No. 6962 Lotus or Stockholm bowl, 7" wide, signed Dalzell, Dalzell-Viking 1990.

1111. No. 1323 Dog figurine, 8" high, signed Dalzell, Dalzell-Viking 1990.

1112. No. 6957 console bowl, Lotus or Stockholm pattern, $13^1/_2$" wide, signed Dalzell, Dalzell-Viking 1990.

1113. No. 1322 Cat figurine, 8" high, signed Dalzell, Dalzell-Viking 1990.

1114. No. 6961 Lotus or Stockholm bowl, 6" wide, signed Dalzell, Dalzell-Viking 1990.

1115. No. 764 Rabbit figurine, 6" long, 3" high, signed Dalzell, Dalzell-Viking 1990.

VICTORIAN, P. 78

Figures 1116–1133 represent items made during or shortly after the Victorian era (from the mid-1880s through the early 1900s). With a few exceptions noted below, they are devoid of markings or stamps of origin.

1116. Round dresser tray, $9^1/_2$" diameter.

1117. Pressed perfume or barber bottle, decorated with gold trim, $6^3/_4$" high.

1118. $7^1/_4$" cigarette box with match holder finial.

1119. Candy bowl in silver basket, $4^1/_2$" diameter.

1120. Covered jar with candlestick finial, $8^1/_4$" high. These jars have also been found with the Mary Gregory style decoration on the sides, and are higher in value.

1121. Pressed vase, 3" high.

1122. 2 oz. tall shot glass, with silver decoration and "Just A Swallow," Depression style, Morgantown Glass Works of Morgantown, West Virginia circa 1930s.

1123. 4 oz. miniature mug, marked "Souvenir of Springfield" in gold decoration on the side, unknown maker.

1124. Perfume bottle with gold decoration, marked "Made in France" on the bottom.

1125. 6" vase with enamel floral pattern.

1126. Decorative pin tray, 6" long.

1127. Footed vase with Fern and Holly pattern, $3^1/_2$" high.

1128. Decanter set, enamel birds and flowers decoration with crushed glass, 13" high, $10^1/_2$" wide. This set consists of a hinged box that conceals an amethyst decanter and six cordials when closed. For illustrative purposes, the box in this photograph has a detached lid to reveal the decanter.

1129. Glove box with scallop decoration, 10$^{1}/_{2}$" long, 4" high.

1130. Hinged, covered box with gold design, 4$^{1}/_{2}$" high.

1131. Art glass candlesticks, cut design of flowers and flower baskets, white glass rim, 6$^{3}/_{4}$" high, signed "Sinclair," H. B. Sinclair Company of Corning, New York 1904.

1132. Art glass console bowl, cut design of flowers and flower baskets, white glass rim, 11$^{3}/_{4}$" diameter, 5" high, signed "Sinclair," H. B. Sinclair Company of Corning, New York 1904.

1133. Covered box, black satin with applied flowers and "Souvenir" in gold.

WESTMORELAND GLASS COMPANY, P. 79

The Westmoreland Glass Company (1888–1984) of Grapeville, Pennsylvania manufactured black glass as early as 1926, and continued intermittently from 1950 through the 1980s. Originally called the Westmoreland Specialty Company, the firm began making mustard and candy jars, then branched out into all colors and types of glass tableware and novelties. Refer to page 5 for information on the company's trademarks.

1134. Santa and Sleigh covered dish, 5$^{1}/_{2}$" high, marked WG, made by Summit Art Glass in old Westmoreland mold 1985.

1135. No. 5 Wren on Perch, 4" high, with label, circa 1970s.

1136. No. 750 basket, 6$^{1}/_{2}$" high, marked WG, circa 1970s.

1137. Santa and Sleigh covered dish, black carnival, 5$^{1}/_{2}$" high, marked WG, made by

Summit Art Glass in old Westmoreland mold 1985.

1138. No. 1921 Star-footed compote, Lotus pattern, 5$^{1}/_{2}$" wide, marked WG, circa 1980s.

1139. No. 1900 Grandma's Slipper with hand-painted decoration, 5" long, marked WG, circa 1980s.

1140. No. 4 Hen covered dish, 4" wide, marked WG, circa 1980s.

1141. No. 1707 7" fan vase or napkin holder, marked WG, circa 1980s.

1142. No. 75 Bull Dog with faceted eyes, 2$^{1}/_{2}$" high, marked WG, 1953.

1143. No. 1 miniature revolver, 5" long, not marked, but made by Westmoreland Glass Company circa 1950s. This is a reproduction of an older version made in the Depression era. The only visible difference is found in the tips of the barrels.

1144. No. 1881 Paneled Grape puff box or covered jelly, 4$^{1}/_{2}$" high, marked WG, circa 1980s.

1145. No. 1902 bud vase, 9" high, marked WG, circa 1970s.

1146. No. 1881 oval basket with split handle, Paneled Grape pattern, 7" long, marked WG, circa 1980s.

1147. No. 1921 Lotus bowl, 11" wide, marked WG, 1967.

1148. No. 1921 Lotus candlesticks, 3$^{1}/_{2}$" high, marked WG, 1967. One Westmoreland catalog suggested turning the candlesticks upside down for use as a mint dish.

Among the Westmoreland Glass Company's Spring 1980 offerings were several vases, trinket boxes, candy jars, a plate and decorator egg, all in black glass with the "Oriental Poppy" decoration. The fan vase *(center row, item F)* is shown without decoration as **Figure 1141** in this book, and other examples of the 8" plate *(item I)* with Forget-Me-Not border are seen in **Figures 860** and **862** of this book.

8566 • Squirrel Tail

8127 • 5 1/2" Candle

8562 • 9" Dolphin

5515 • 6 1/2" 3 Light Candelabra

2171 • 7 1/2" Round Ftd.

8563 • 4" Dolphin

5513 • 4 1/2" 1 Light Candelabra

Black

This assortment of candlesticks from an undated Dalzell-Viking catalog features several well-known pieces in black. The 3-light candelabrum is seen as **Figure 1106** in this book, the Squirrel Tail as **Figure 1081**, and the large and small Dolphins as **Figures 1084** and **1097** respectively. The Dolphin pieces were part of Westmoreland's Line No. 1049. The Westmoreland version was not marked, but very few were made in black. The Viking Glass version had the company label, and the Dalzell version was signed Dalzell.

Top photo: This Corningware Classic Black selection was advertised as new for 1992. All three pieces appear as **Figures 405–407** in this book. *Bottom photo:* Factice bottles such as these (and **Figure 813**) made for Maxim's de Paris were often filled with colored liquid and used only for display.

THE BLACK TIE COLLECTION

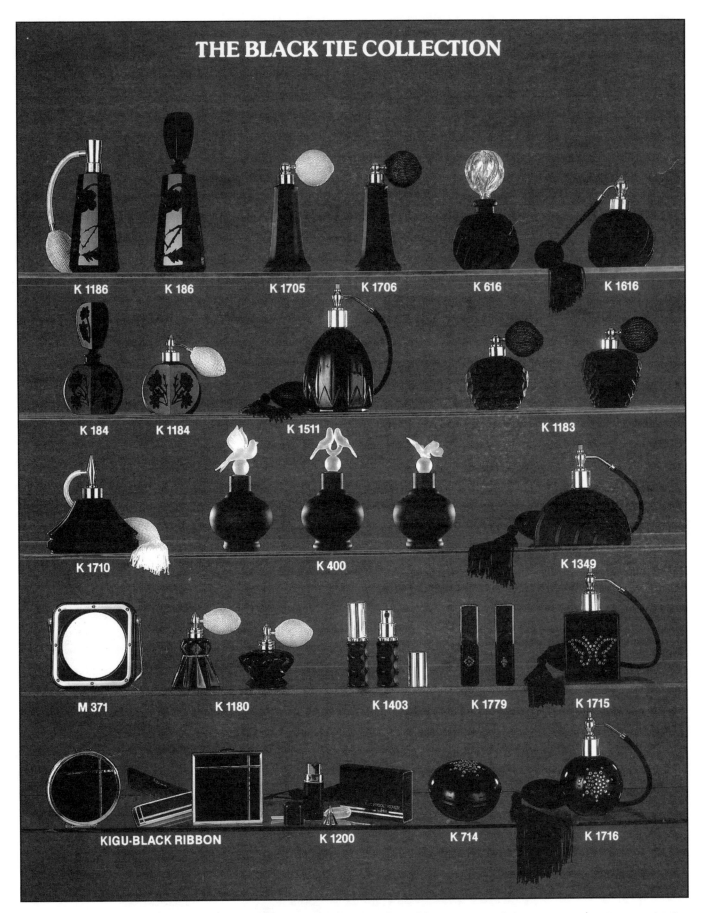

The Irving W. Rice & Company 1985/1986 catalog features page after page of fine imports, including European boutique accessories and perfume bottles. The Black Tie Collection (Rice, p. 3) features several bottles shown in this book. From top to bottom: K 186 appears as **Figure 793**, K 1184 as **Figure 817**, K 1183 as **Figures 804** and **811**, K 1180 as **Figures 809** and **816**, and K 1403 as **Figure 812**.

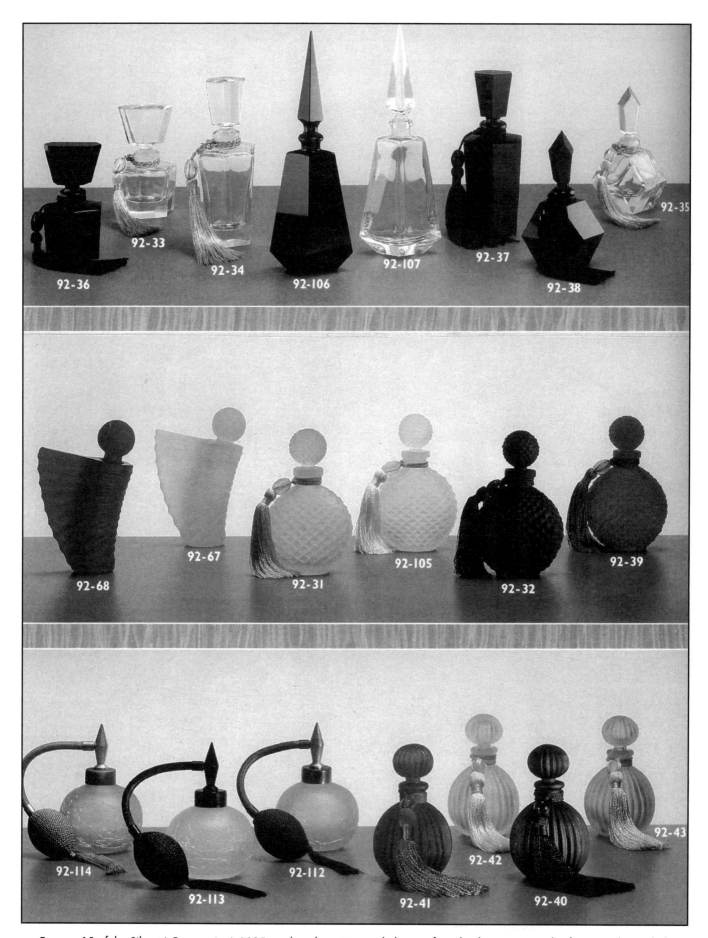

92-33

92-34

92-106

92-107

92-37

92-38

92-35

92-36

92-68

92-67

92-31

92-105

92-32

92-39

92-114

92-113

92-112

92-41

92-42

92-40

92-43

From p. 18 of the Silvestri Corporation's 1985 catalog, these imported glass perfume bottles range in color from peach to cobalt.

The Silvestri Corporation's 1985 catalog features art glass selections varying in style from Roman to Japanese, and in color from red hot to smoke. These art glass vases were designed by Charles A. Berry and were featured as part of the Bauhaus Collection.

Right: Sasaki Crystal Black Tie collection. This Japanese imported set consists of place-card holders, a dinner bell, ring holder, smoke set, bud vase, powder jar and pin jar.

Below: An assortment of lead crystal barware.

This sales sheet for Sasaki stemware advertises mouth blown full lead crystal. Two patterns, the Royale and the Noir, prominently feature black.

SASAKI
CRYSTAL

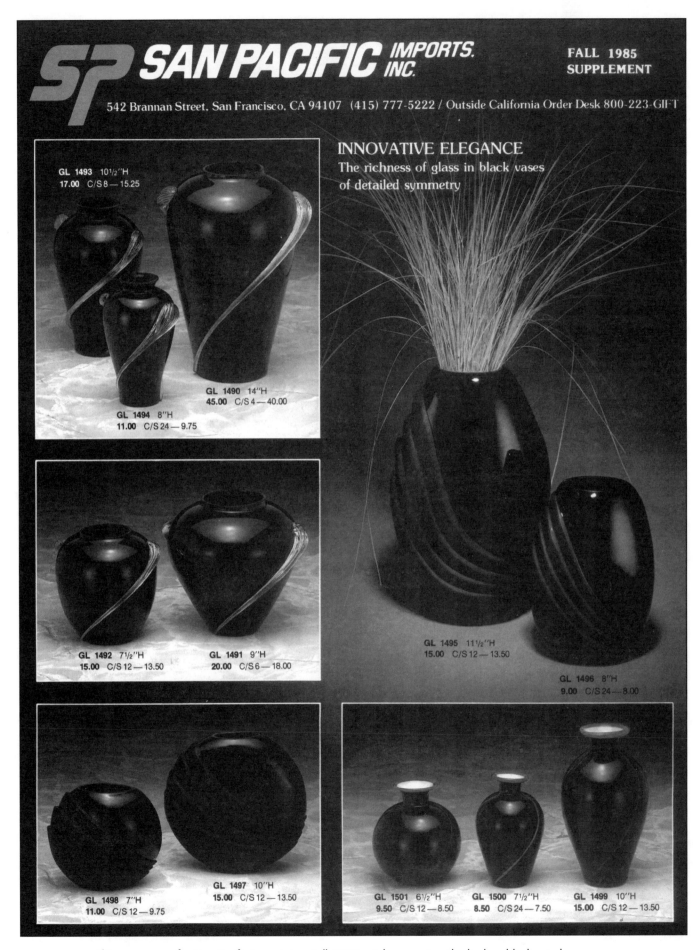

SAN PACIFIC IMPORTS. INC.

542 Brannan Street, San Francisco, CA 94107 (415) 777-5222 / Outside California Order Desk 800-223-GIFT

GL 1493 10½"H
17.00 C/S 8 — 15.25

GL 1494 8"H
11.00 C/S 24 — 9.75

GL 1490 14"H
45.00 C/S 4 — 40.00

INNOVATIVE ELEGANCE
The richness of glass in black vases
of detailed symmetry

GL 1492 7½"H
15.00 C/S 12 — 13.50

GL 1491 9"H
20.00 C/S 6 — 18.00

GL 1495 11½"H
15.00 C/S 12 — 13.50

GL 1496 8"H
9.00 C/S 24 — 8.00

GL 1498 7"H
11.00 C/S 12 — 9.75

GL 1497 10"H
15.00 C/S 12 — 13.50

GL 1501 6½"H
9.50 C/S 12 — 8.50

GL 1500 7½"H
8.50 C/S 24 — 7.50

GL 1499 10"H
15.00 C/S 12 — 13.50

This cover page for San Pacific Imports Inc. Fall 1985 catalog prominently displays black art glass vases.

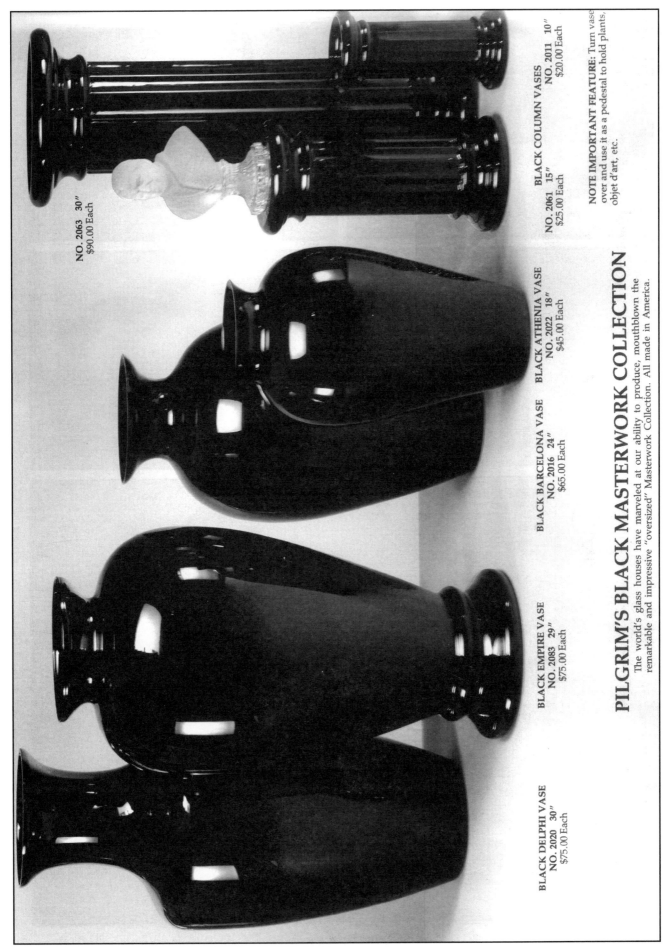

PILGRIM'S BLACK MASTERWORK COLLECTION

The world's glass houses have marveled at our ability to produce, mouthblown the remarkable and impressive "oversized" Masterwork Collection. All made in America.

BLACK DELPHI VASE
NO. 2020 30"
$75.00 Each

BLACK EMPIRE VASE
NO. 2083 29"
$75.00 Each

BLACK BARCELONA VASE
NO. 2016 24"
$65.00 Each

BLACK ATHENIA VASE
NO. 2022 18"
$45.00 Each

NO. 2063 30"
$90.00 Each

BLACK COLUMN VASES
NO. 2061 15"
$25.00 Each

NO. 2011 10"
$20.00 Each

NOTE IMPORTANT FEATURE: Turn vase over and use it as a pedestal to hold plants, objet d'art, etc.

From Pilgrim's 1991 catalog (p. 24), this collection of oversized vases is so versatile, that the suggestion is made to invert them for use as pedestals.

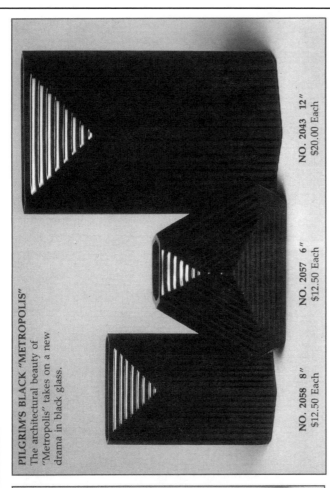

PILGRIM'S BLACK "METROPOLIS"
The architectural beauty of "Metropolis" takes on a new drama in black glass.

NO. 2043 12"
$20.00 Each

NO. 2057 6"
$12.50 Each

NO. 2058 8"
$12.50 Each

BLACK KYOTO BOWL
Elegant simplicity.

NO. 2084 11" $17.50 Each

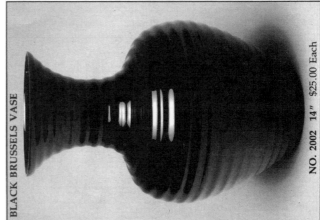

BLACK BRUSSELS VASE

NO. 2002 14" $25.00 Each

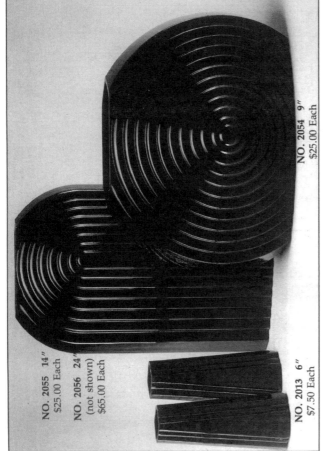

NO. 2055 14"
$25.00 Each

NO. 2056 24"
(not shown)
$65.00 Each

NO. 2054 9"
$25.00 Each

NO. 2013 6"
$7.50 Each

BLACK GRECIAN VASE

NO. 2079 10" $17.50 Each

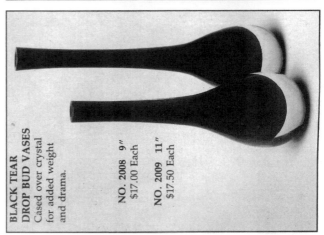

BLACK TEAR DROP BUD VASES
Cased over crystal for added weight and drama.

NO. 2008 9"
$17.00 Each

NO. 2009 11"
$17.50 Each

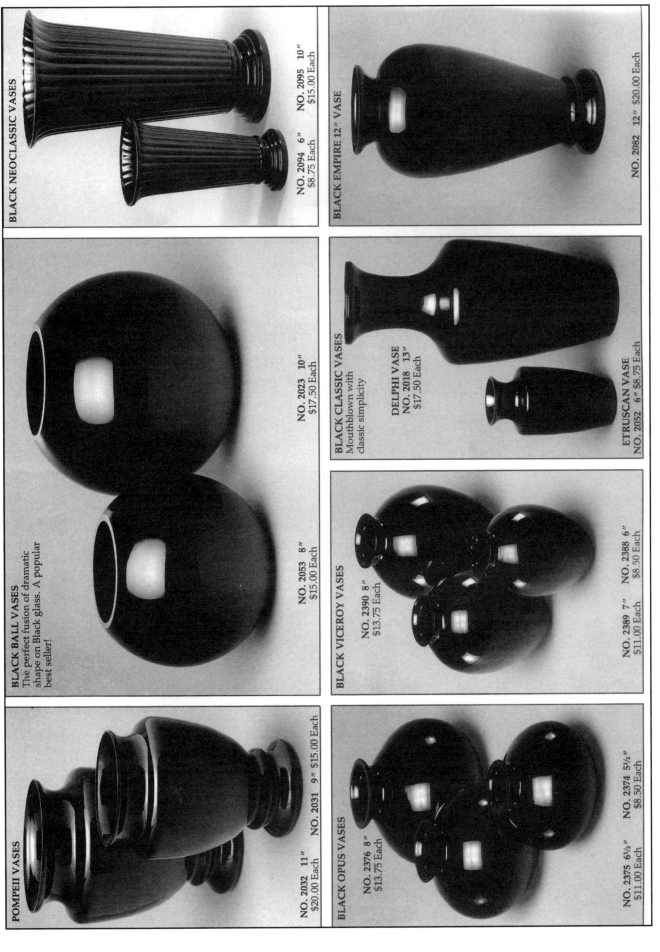

BLACK NEOCLASSIC VASES

NO. 2094 6"
$8.75 Each

NO. 2095 10"
$15.00 Each

BLACK EMPIRE 12" VASE

NO. 2082 12" $20.00 Each

BLACK BALL VASES
The perfect fusion of dramatic shape on Black glass. A popular best seller!

NO. 2053 8"
$15.00 Each

NO. 2023 10"
$17.50 Each

BLACK CLASSIC VASES
Mouthblown with classic simplicity

DELPHI VASE
NO. 2018 13"
$17.50 Each

ETRUSCAN VASE
NO. 2052 6" $8.75 Each

POMPEII VASES

NO. 2032 11"
$20.00 Each

NO. 2031 9" $15.00 Each

BLACK VICEROY VASES

NO. 2390 8"
$13.75 Each

NO. 2389 7"
$11.00 Each

NO. 2388 6"
$8.50 Each

BLACK OPUS VASES

NO. 2376 8"
$13.75 Each

NO. 2375 6½"
$11.00 Each

NO. 2374 5½"
$8.50 Each

Above: The Pilgrim Glass Corporation's 1991 catalog (pp. 25–26) shows these pieces on display from the Black Collection.

the Legend
of the
Secret Slipper

Knights of yore returned from the crusades bearing wonderful gifts for their loved ones. Highly valued among these were the beautifully-decorated "Secret Slippers" with their long and pointed upturned toes. Because the slippers had magical powers to ward off evil and bring great happiness, they were given as tokens of the highest esteem to very special people.

Fenton revives this legend through its handmade glass slipper. As the knights of long ago followed a lofty code of conduct, Fenton glassmakers follow a tradition of quality craftsmanship in every secret slipper created.

Right: The 5" "Secret Slipper" is shown here with written medieval legend and display stand in the Fenton Art Glass Company's 1995 catalog. The No. 2931 slipper appears in black glass as **Figure 176** in this book.

2931 YS   2931 YU   2931YM   2931 YR

2931 YT   2931 SL

5145 S8
*Special Egg

Each Egg on Stand is 4"
in Height.

5145 S7

5145 S6

5145 S2   5145 S4   5145 S5

5145 S3

Left: This "Collectible Eggs" assortment was offered in the same catalog, each egg handpainted in a different motif. The No. 5145 S2 egg appears as **Figure 171**.

Index

Bibliography

Archer, Margaret and Douglas. *The Collector's Encyclopedia of Glass Candlesticks*. Paducah, KY: Collector Books.

Baker, Gary E., et al (Ed. Gerald I. Reilly). *Wheeling Glass 1829–1939, Collection of the Oglebay Institute Glass Museum*. Wheeling, WV: Oglebay Institute, 1994.

Belknap, E. M. *Milk Glass*. New York: Crown Publishers, 1959.

Bickenheuser, Fred. *Tiffin Glassmasters, Book 1*. Grove City, OH: Glassmasters Publications, 1979.

---. *Tiffin Glassmasters, Book 2*. Grove City, OH: Glassmasters Publications, 1981.

Burkholder, John and D. Thomas O'Connor. *Kemple Glass: 1945–1970*. Marietta, OH: Antique Publications, 1997.

Collectable Glass, British Glass, Book 4. Wallace-Homestead Publishing.

H. C. Fry Glass Society. *The Collector's Encyclopedia to Fry Glass*. Paducah, KY: Collector Books, 1990.

Garmon, Lee and Dick Spencer. *Glass Animals of the Depression Era*. Paducah, KY: Collector Books, 1993.

Glass Review, The. Various issues, September 1981–November 1986.

Hastin, Bud. *Avon Bottle Encyclopedia*.

Heacock, William. *Fenton Glass: The First Twenty-Five Years*. Marietta, OH: O-Val Advertising Corp., 1978.

---. *Fenton Glass: The Second Twenty-Five Years*. Marietta, OH: O-Val Advertising Corp., 1980.

---. *Fenton Glass: The Third Twenty-Five Years*. Marietta, OH: O-Val Advertising Corp., 1989.

Kovar, Lorraine. *Westmoreland Glass, 1950–1984, Volume I*. Marietta, OH: Antique Publications, 1991.

---. *Westmoreland Glass, 1950–1984, Volume II*. Marietta, OH: Antique Publications, 1991.

---. *Westmoreland Glass, Vol. 3, 1888–1940*. Marietta, OH: Antique Publications, 1997.

Measell, James. *New Martinsville Glass, 1900–1944*. Marietta, OH: Antique Publications, 1994.

Measell, James and Berry Wiggins. *Great American Glass of the Roaring 20s and Depression Era*. Marietta, OH: Antique Publications, 1998.

National Imperial Glass Collectors Society (Ed. James Measell). *Imperial Glass Encyclopedia, Vol. I, A–Cane*. Marietta, OH: Antique Publications, 1995.

---. *Imperial Glass Encyclopedia, Vol. II, Cape Cod–L*. Marietta, OH: Antique Publications, 1997.

Newbound, Betty. *The Collector's Encyclopedia of Milk Glass*. Paducah, KY: Collector Books.

---. *The Glass Collector's Almanac*. Union Lake, MI: Self-published, 1987.

Newman, Harold. *An Illustrated Dictionary of Glass*. London: Thames and Hudson Ltd., 1977.

Over, Naomi. *Ruby Glass of the 20th Century*. Marietta, OH: Antique Publications, 1990.

Sferrazza, Julie. *Farber Brothers Krome-Kraft: A Guide for Collectors*. Marietta, OH: Antique Publications, 1988.

Snyder, Jeffrey B. *Morgantown Glass, From Depression Glass through the 1960s*.

Toohey, Marlena. *A Collector's Guide to Black Glass*. Marietta, OH: Antique Publications, 1988.

Weatherman, Hazel Marie. *Colored Glassware of the Depression Era 2*. Paducah, KY: Collector Books.

Welker, John and Elizabeth. *Pressed Glass in America: Encyclopedia of the First Hundred Years, 1825–1925*. Ivyland, PA: Antique Acres Press, 1985.

Whitmyer, Margaret and Kenn. *Fenton Art Glass, 1907–1939*. Paducah, KY: Collector Books, 1996.

Wilson, Charles West. *Westmoreland Glass, Identification and Value Guide*. Paducah, KY: Collector Books, 1996.

◄ 1999 Value Guide ►

This section of the book is intended to provide current values for almost all of the black glass items shown in color on pages 18–80. Values are listed in order by the figure numbers that were assigned each piece. These figure numbers also correspond with descriptive captions on pages 7–15, and 81–107 of this book. Prices reflect items that are in excellent condition. In a few cases, no price is listed due to rarity.

The reader should note that this guide to values is based on my own buying and collecting experience. Variability in prices abounds according to rarity, condition and geographical location. Neither the publisher nor the author can accept responsibility or liability for losses incurred by persons using this guide, whether due to typographical errors or other reasons.

Figure	Price	Figure	Price	Figure	Price	Figure	Price	Figure	Price
1.	$ 11	34.	$ 5	71.	$ 20	110.	$150	144.	$ 30 ea
2.	7	35.	3	72.	35	111.	15	145.	85
3.	10	36.	3	73.	15	112.	15	146.	35 ea
4.	7	37.	3	74.	20	113.	35	147.	10
5.	9	38.	20	75.	15	114.	15	148.	8
6.	8	39.	25	76.	15	115.	15	149.	12
7.	6	40.	20	77.	20	116.	20	150.	5
8.	11	41.	25	78.	15	117.	300	151.	5
9.	8	42.	20	79.	15	118.	150	152.	5
10.	5	43.	25	80.	15	119.	20	153.	5
11.	8	44.	20	81.	15	120.	35	154.	8
12.	8	45.	35	82.	35 pr	121.	35	155.	10
13.	4	46.	20	83.	30	122.	25	156.	6
14.	12	47-50.	65 set	84-89.	150 set	123.	25	157.	8
15.	6	51.	20	90.	20	124.	25	158.	6
16.	7	52.	25	91.	20	125.	15	159.	6
17.	15 pr	53.	35	92.	20	126.	20	160.	45
18.	10	54.	20	93.	15	127.	20	161.	65
19.	12	55.	15	94.	15	128.	20	162.	55
20.	9	56.	15	95.	10	129.	20	163.	40
21.	15	57.	18	96.	10	130.	45	164.	67
22.	7	58.	18	97.	20	131.	15	165.	25
23.	15	59.	15	98.	20	132.	35	166.	35
24.	15	60.	15	99.	15	133.	20	167.	32
25.	2	61.	15	100.	20	134.	20	168.	32
26.	8	62.	35	101.	20	135.	20	169.	45
27.	5	63.	20	102.	20	136.	55	170.	35
28.	15	64.	20	103.	75	137.	75	171.	35
29.	35	65.	20	104.	20	138.	100	172.	25
30a.	15	66.	35	105.	12	139.	20	173.	32
30b.	15	67.	20	106.	35	140.	45	174.	55 pr
31.	15	68.	20	107.	40	141.	35	175.	20
32.	3	69.	18	108.	80	142.	65	176.	40
33.	3	70.	20	109.	20	143.	65	177.	42

Figure	Price	Figure	Price	Figure	Price	Figure	Price	Figure	Price
178.	$ 35	227.	$ 10	264.	$ 20	316.	$ 65	365.	$ 45
179.	35	228.	8	265.	20	317.	20	366.	25
180.	145 rare	229.	45	266.	250 rare	318.	18	367.	125
181.	150 rare	230.	8	267.	20	319.	125	368.	20
182.	75	231.	75	268.	250 rare	320.	32	369.	30
183.	350	232.	40	269.	40 pr	321.	35	370.	15
184.	15	233.	25	270.	45	322.	120	371.	35
185.	350	234.	5	271.	38	323.	120	372.	35
186.	35	235.	75	272-75.	40 set	324.	150 set	373.	25
187.	350	236.	20	276.	45	325.	85	374.	45
188.	25	237.	30	277.	17	326.	65	375.	65
189.	40	238.	65	278.	18	327.	40	376.	3
190.	40	239.	25	279.	150	328.	35	377.	3
191.	35	240.	5	280.	1,000	329a-t.	1 - 5 ea	378.	20
192.	35	241.	35	281.	150	330.	85	379.	3
193.	110	242.	35	282.	300	331.	35	380.	5
194.	45	243.	15	283.	45	332.	38	381.	10
195.	35	244.	60	284.	65	333.	25 pr	382.	2
196.	25	245.	55	285.	125	334.	20 pr	383.	1
197.	20	246.	10	286.	45	335.	20 pr	384.	8 pr
198.	20	247.	20	287.	28	336.	35	385.	5
199.	20	248.	10	288.	18	337.	35	386.	5
200.	20	248.a	3	289.	25	338.	15 pr	387.	8
201.	20	248.b	3	290.	18	339.	65	388.	7
202.	20	248.c	3	291.	45	340.	45	389.	9
203.	35	249.	10	292.	48	341.	10	390.	1
204.	30	249.a	30	293.	125	342.	40 pr	391.	1
205.	30	249.b	3	294.	150	343.	20	392.	10 set
206.	25	249.c	3	295.	65	344.	10	393.	25
207.	25	250.	50	296.	75	345.	40	394.	3
208.	20	251.	100	297.	20	346.	25 pr	395.	25
209.	125	252.	8	298.	20	347.	65	396.	10
210.	25	253.	15	299.	3	348.	25	397.	3
211.	15	253a.	5	300.	65	349.	25	398.	3
212.	25	253b.	8	301.	20	350.	35	399.	3
213.	110	253c.	8	302.	20	351.	45	400.	3
214.	225 rare	253d.	5	303.	20	352.	25	401.	3
215.	45	253e.	3	304.	20	353.	20	402.	10
216.	35	253f.	5	305.	20	354.	35	403.	10
217.	40	254.	15	306.	15	355.	30	404.	5
218.	10	255.	12	307.	35	356.	25	405.	14
219.	8	256.	45	308.	15	357.	30	406.	25
220.	5	257.	25	309.	10	358.	35	407.	15
221.	12	258.	50	310.	5	359.	65	408.	20
222.	6	259.	15	311.	45	360.	25	409.	10
223.	10	260.	5	312.	35 pr	361.	115	410.	3
224.	35	261.	18	313.	35	362.	35	411.	10
225.	20	262.	20	314.	15	363.	25	412.	25
226.	20	263.	20	315.	38	364.	35	413.	5

Figure	Price		Figure	Price		Figure	Price		Figure	Price		Figure	Price	
414.	$ 5		463.	$ 23		505a-b.	$ 6 ea		550.	$ 35		600.	$ 75	
415.	8		464.	20			12 set		551.	75		601.	150 pr	
416.	8		465.	30		506.	12		552.	22		602.	135	
417.	8		466.	45		507.	10		553.	40		603.	35	
418.	10		467.	20		508a-b.	5 ea		554.	22		604.	35	
419.	15		468.	45			10 set		555.	45		605.	150	
420.	25		469.	65		509.	10		556.	20		606.	65	
421.	5		470.	150		510.	6		557.	22		607.	48	
422.	15		471.	35		511.	10		558.	18		608.	85	
423.	20		472.	35		512.	12		559.	20		609.	65	
424.	35		473.	37		513a-b.	6 ea		560.	25		610.	100	
425.	20		474.	35			12 set		561.	25		611.	165	
426.	15		475.	35		514a-b.	6 ea		562.	12		612.	45	
427.	15		476.	125			12 set		563.	38		613.	25	
428.	15		477.	45 pr		515.	12		564.	15		614.	48	
429.	10		478.	45		516.	10		565.	22		615.	45	
430.	15		479.	15		517a-b.	5 ea		566.	15		616.	65	
431.	20 set		480.	45			10 set		567.	22		617.	38	
432.	5		481.	30		518.	10		568.	15		618.	28	
433.	25		482.	200		519.	15		569.	5		619.	35	
434.	15		483.	25 each		520.	10		570.	45		620.	32	
435.	25		484.	45		521.	15 set		571.	20		621.	35	
436.	15		485.	60		522.	15 pr		572.	20		622.	20	
437.	15		486.	25		523.	15		573.	30		623.	60	
438.	10		487.	85		524.	5		574.	10		624.	30	
439.	15		488.	25		525a-f.	6 ea		575.	21		625.	35	
440.	15		489.	25 set		526.	12		576.	10		626.	27	
441.	7		490.	35 set		527.	10		577.	5		627.	45	
442.	7		491.	18		528.	6		578.	8		628.	38	
443.	20 pr		492.	20		529.	6		579.	22		629.	25	
444.	20		493.	170 set		530.	15		580.	10		630.	25	
445.	45 pr			35 c/s		531.	21		581.	10		631.	20	
446.	35			35 s/p		532.	12		582.	10		632.	35	
447.	35 pr		(rare)	100 tray		533.	10		583.	10		633.	20	
448.	7		494.	20		534.	15		584.	15		634.	20	
449.	15		495a-b.	10 ea		535.	8		585.	10		635.	35	
450.	7			20 set		536.	8		586.	10		636.	15	
451.	12		496a-b.	10 ea		537.	8		587.	5		637.	18	
452.	5			20 set		538.	15		588.	250		638.	35	
453.	20		497.	22		539.	8		589.	18		639.	36	
454.	22		498.	40		540.	8		590.	15		640.	95	
455.	20		499.	15		541.	8		591.	45		641a-b.	25 ea	
456.	35		500a-b.	7.50 ea		542.	8		592.	250		642.	20	
457.	45			15 set		543.	8		593.	250		643.	25	
458.	85		501a-b.	5 ea		544.	8		594.	45		644.	30	
459.	125			10 set		545.	8		595.	20		645.	65	
460.	60		502.	10		546.	45		596.	185		646.	32	
461.	65		503.	10		547.	16 pr		597.	53		647.	125	
462.	35		504a-b.	5 ea		548.	125		598.	25		648.	20	
				10 set		549.	35		599.	45		649.	65	

Figure	Price	Figure	Price	Figure	Price	Figure	Price	Figure	Price
650.	$ 45	698.	$ 45	747.	$ 18	796.	$ 20	845.	$ 35
651.	50	699.	15 ea	748.	15	797.	10	846.	20
652.	25	700.	20	749.	15	798.	10	847.	35
653.	20	701.	75	750.	15	799.	20	848.	35
654.	40 pr	702.	25	751.	18	800.	25	849.	35
655.	34	703.	10	752.	18	801.	20	850.	20
656.	45	704.	30	753.	18	802.	25	851.	20
657.	56 set	705.	40	754.	20	803.	20	852.	25
658.	20	706.	80	755.	25	804.	20	853.	5
659.	48 pr	707.	100	756.	20	805.	150	854.	125
660.	165	708.	45	757.	25	806.	15	855.	50
661a-b.	20 ea	709.	15	758.	35	807.	20	856.	45
	40 set	710.	25	759.	25	808.	25	857.	35
662.	85	711.	25	760.	20	809.	20	858.	40
663.	68	712.	18	761.	20	810.	25	859.	20
664.	52	713.	45	762.	10	811.	20	860.	75
665.	65	714.	25	763.	20	812.	15	861.	35
666.	55	715.	25	764.	25	813.	400	862.	75
667.	45	716.	25	765.	25	814.	20	863.	25
668.	40	717.	40	766.	20 pr	815.	20	864.	95
669.	75	718.	30 pr	767.	25	816.	20	865.	10
670.	40	719.	42	768.	20	817.	25	866.	40
671.	25	720.	25	769.	40 pr	818.	3	867.	35
672.	35	721.	35	770.	20	819.	150	868.	85
673.	45	722.	25	771.	20	820.	20	869.	65
674.	40	723.	45	772.	20	821.	50	870.	150
675.	45	724.	18	773.	20	822.	100	871.	150
676.	20	725.	22	774.	20	823.	10	872.	50
677.	25	726.	18	775.	20	824.	10	873.	15
678.	45	727.	18	776.	20	825.	5	873.	15
679.	15	728.	20	777.	10	826.	10	874.	15
680.	12	729.	18	778.	18	827.	5	875.	15
681.	15	730.	20	779.	20	828.	10	876.	15
682.	45	731.	45	780.	10	829.	400	877.	15
683.	45 pr	732.	56	781.	10	830.	110	878.	15
684.	46	733.	100	782.	15	831.	32	879.	15
685.	100	734.	15	783.	20	832.	35	880.	15
686.	20	735.	40	784.	15	833.	35	881.	15
687.	65	736.	65	785.	40 set	834.	35	882.	15
688.	20	737.	50	786.	40 set	835.	25	883.	15
689.	110	738.	20	787.	40 set	836.	35	884.	15
690.	30	739.	50	788.	10	837.	35	885.	15
691.	65	740.	30	789.	8	838.	35	886.	30
692.	18	741.	15	790.	20	839.	45	887.	30
693.	18	742.	20	791.	10	840.	35	888.	20
694.	18	743.	38	792.	25	841.	35	889.	25
695.	18	744.	20	793.	35	842.	35	890.	45
696.	24	745.	40	794.	25	843.	35	891.	15
697.	25	746.	75	795.	25	844.	20	892.	30

Figure	Price	Figure	Price	Figure	Price	Figure	Price	Figure	Price
893.	$ 15	942.	$ 15	1001.	$ 20	1054.	$ 35	1103.	$ 24
894.	15	943.	50	1002.	35	1055.	35	1104.	145
895.	15	944.	50	1003.	35	1056.	15	1105.	125
896.	35	945.	50	1004.	15	1057.	20	1106.	100
897.	25	946.	20	1005.	15	1058.	25	1107.	125
898.	5	947.	20	1006-10.	10	1059.	20	1108.	145
899.	10	948-54.	10 ea	1011.	10	1060.	10	1109.	75
900.	10	955.	20	1012.	10	1061.	20	1110.	35
901.	18	956.	22	1013.	20	1062.	25	1111.	95
902.	5	957.	10	1014.	20	1063.	45	1112.	45
903.	5	958.	15	1015.	25	1064.	35	1113.	95
904.	10	959.	15	1016.	20	1065.	35	1114.	35
905.	20	960.	25	1017.	10	1066.	75	1115.	75
906.	20	961.	25	1018.	5	1067.	95	1116.	85
907a-d.	25 ea	962.	25	1019.	5	1068.	225	1117.	110
908.	35	963.	20	1020.	5	1069.	125	1118.	75
909.	45	964.	10	1021.	5	1070.	20	1119.	45
910.	85	965.	25	1022.	5	1071.	35	1120.	45 ea
911.	25	966.	25	1023.	5	1072.	25	1121.	25
912.	15	967.	20	1024.	3	1073.	300 pr	1122.	35
913.	35	968.	65	1025.	22	1074.	48	1123.	45
914.	35	969.	15	1026.	10	1075.	50	1124.	125
915.	15	970.	25	1027.	15	1076.	28	1125.	60
916.	40	971.	25	1028.	10 ea	1077.	28	1126.	45
917.	20	972.	25	1029.	15 pr	1078.	70	1127.	38
918.	30	973.	10	1030.	5	1079.	35	1128.	500
919.	20	974.	20	1031.	15	1080.	60	1129.	145
920.	30	975.	20	1032.	10 pr	1081.	28	1130.	135
921.	20	976.	20	1033.	20	1082.	20	1131.	500 pr
922.	25	977.	10	1034.	40	1083.	20	1132.	500
923.	20	978.	45	1035.	45	1084.	125 pr	1133.	125
924.	20	979.	22	1036.	5	1085.	45 set	1134.	40
925.	25	980.	15	1037.	15	1086.	50	1135.	30
926.	15	981.	20	1038.	20	1087.	25	1136.	25
927.	10	982.	35	1039.	30	1088.	85	1137.	40
928.	20	983.	15	1040.	25	1089.	20	1138.	30
929.	15	984.	18	1041.	35	1090.	20	1139.	35
930.	10	985.	18	1042.	25	1091.	45	1140.	30
931.	15	986.	25	1043.	30	1092.	20	1141.	22
932.	12	987.	20	1044.	25	1093.	20	1142.	25
933.	10	988.	35	1045a-b.	25 set	1094.	60	1143.	78
934.	15	989.	35	1046.	15 pr	1095.	20	1144.	28
935.	10	990.	10	1047.	45	1096.	20	1145.	20
936.	15	991.	35	1048.	25	1097.	50 pr	1146.	28
937.	50	992.	15	1049.	12.50	1098.	65	1147.	60
938.	50	993.	12	1050.	15	1099.	64	1148.	70 pr
939.	50	994.	10	1051.	10	1100.	44 set		
940.	15	995-99.	10 each	1052.	35	1101.	46		
941.	15	1000.	25	1053.	50	1102.	34		

Notes